Lawns and Playing Fields

LAWNS AND
PLAYING FIELDS

by

F. J. REED

FABER AND FABER LTD
24 Russell Square
London

First published in mcml
by Faber and Faber Limited
24 Russell Square London W.C.1
Printed in Great Britain by
Latimer Trend & Co Ltd Plymouth

Acknowledgments

Parks Superintendents, Head Groundsmen, Head Greenkeepers and their staffs have assisted me for a number of years, conducting trials and furnishing practical reports. I tender my sincere thanks to them, and to the following who have been kind enough to allow me to use photographs and blocks: Messrs. Burt, Boulton and Haywood; W. Hargreaves & Co.; Heath & Heather; Hurst & Son; Mr. I. G. Lewis, N.D.A.; The Ministry of Agriculture & Fisheries; The Borough of Southampton; and Ryder & Son (1920) Ltd.

My thanks are also expressed to the Editor of *Parks, Golf Courses & Sports Grounds* for permission to include material extracted from articles written by me in various numbers of that journal.

It will be noted that throughout the work no attempt has been made to convert botanical descriptions of lawn grasses, weeds, and weed grasses into so-called 'simple language'. I have followed closely the methods adopted by De Candolle in the *Flore Française*, and the excellent system of *The British Flora* by Bentham & Hooker, with the object not only of describing a plant but also of assisting to increase the botanical knowledge of all who are interested in fine turf.

Contents

❯❯❯❯❯ ◦ ❮❮❮❮❮

Illustrations

❧❧❧❧ ⬦ ❧❧❧❧

Chapter One

Origin of the Greensward

⫸⫸⫸⫸ ∘ ⫷⫷⫷⫷

Through the ages the praise of the green lawn has been sung in poetry and prose. Few will disagree with Bacon,[1] who says: 'The green hath two pleasures, the one because nothing is more pleasant to the eye than green grass finely shorn, the other because it will give you a fair alley in the midst.'

The lawn is to-day, and has been through the years, the verdant background for a pageantry of garden colour, and while its origins are remote, the evolution of British lawns is due to the love of our people for garden beauty and their deep-rooted enjoyment of outdoor sports. Green lawns, perchance like a meadow interspersed with flowers, are considered to have formed part of Persian gardens as long ago as 500 B.C. for it is recorded[2] that: 'Wherever the Persian King, Cyrus, resides or whatever place he visits in his dominions, he takes care that the Paradises shall be filled with everything, both beautiful and useful, the soil can produce.'

The Greeks copied the gardening of the Persians and while progress did not match that of the sister art, architecture, the vale of Tempé described by Ælianus and the public gardens of Athens mentioned by Plutarch indicate that the Greeks were alive to the beauties of verdant scenery. The first brief mention of a Roman garden is made by Livy, 354 B.C., but Pliny the younger in his *Letters* describes at length his gardens and pleasure grounds. Here the lawn is known as the 'pratulum' or the 'little meadow in the garden'. This little meadow was no doubt gay with flowers, but it was a lawn—grown not for the feeding of cattle, but for its beauty. Loudon[3] was of the opinion that Pliny's villas gave a bias to the European taste in gardening up to the end of the seventeenth century and therefore the garden lawn, perhaps not so extensive

[1] Bacon: Essay, *Of Gardens.*
[2] Xen. Memorab. lib. V, p. 829.
[3] Loudon, J. E.: *Encyclopædia of Gardening,* 1828.

13

as in later years, evolved from the flower-starred little meadows of the Persians.

The Roman conquest of Britain brought with it the culture of the conquerors. Strabo, writing in the fourth century, tells us: 'The people of Britain are generally ignorant of the art of cultivating gardens.' Remains of Roman villas show that gardening was established and doubtless the 'pratulum' formed part of the garden scheme.

With the departure of the Romans, culture declined and although the word 'lawn' is probably derived from the Celtic 'lann'—an enclosure or waste—lawns survived only as the shorter grass in orchards and later in the monastic cloister.

Gardening is a peaceful art; war and cultivation for beauty's sake do not walk hand in hand, and consequently it was not until the Normans had established themselves that any further advance can be traced. There is little doubt that the bowling green was the forerunner of the present-day lawn. The game of bowls is one of the oldest of our outdoor games and emphasizes the important part that outdoor sport and recreation have played in the development of the greensward. Bowls can be traced to the thirteenth century with certainty, and conjecturally to the twelfth. A thirteenth-century manuscript[1] contains a drawing of two players aiming at a small cone; and another of the same century shows bowls and a jack.

Archery was brought to great perfection in England during the reign of Edward III and the monarch devoted such attention to the encouragement of the art that he forbade the playing of bowls—the popularity of which, it was contended, would jeopardize the practice of archery.

Cricket,[2] in its elementary form of club-ball, was played in the thirteenth century according to pictorial evidence, but the first written reference is made at the beginning of the fourteenth century in the wardrobe accounts of Edward I, and relating to certain items disbursed on behalf of the young Prince Edward.

The playing of bowls and cricket had an early influence upon fine turf production, for these games could not be played in long meadow-grass; and while bowling greens were often formed from dwarf herbs, the full enjoyment of both games demanded a close, short turf—a factor of great importance.

The kicking of inflated bladders on public greens[3] became a popular diversion for youths of the lower classes during the sixteenth century, but

[1] Royal Library, Windsor (No. 20, E. IV).
[2] *Chronique d'Angleterre, depuis Ethelbert jusqu'à Henry III.*
[3] Dean Hill: *Football Through the Years.*

the game did not gain immediate popularity with people of more mature years because of the shouting and hallooing which were its accompaniment. This was the beginning of football, and the shouting and hallooing are still with us although to-day not confined to the players.

A statute of 1511 confirmed previous enactments against unlawful games and further enjoined that anyone playing bowls outside his own garden or orchard was liable to a penalty of six shillings and eightpence. The monarch, however, had bowling greens constructed at Whitehall and Nonsuch, and Henry VIII who, as a youth, was an athlete, found joy in bowling a wood, as have many men and women in more recent centuries.

Shakespeare mentions the game and reveals that bias, introduced in the sixteenth century, was known to him.

> *'Twill make me think the world is full of rubs*
> *and that my fortune runs against the bias.*
>
> (*Richard II*, Act III, Scene 4)

Thomas Wilson (1601–?1653), a Puritan divine, went far to convert the people of Maidstone to the proper observance of the Sabbath. According to a writer of the period, this was 'formerly a very profane town inasmuch as I have seen morrice dancing, cudgel playing, stool ball, crickets and many other sports openly and publicly on the Lord's Day'. It would appear that thus early there was a need for organized communal recreation; the heath, common, and green in town and village serving as the medieval park and recreation ground.

The love of the Englishman for competitive games of skill defied many obstacles. In 1654, the churchwardens of Eltham fined seven of their parishioners for playing cricket on the Lord's Day, but cricket and other sports were gaining in popularity and clubs were formed. There is evidence of the existence of the St. Albans Cricket Club in 1666 and later came the heyday of Hambledon, 'the cradle of English cricket'.

The 'Royal and Ancient game of Golf' was as yet confined to seaside 'links' where the natural turf provided suitable conditions. Thus it will be noted that the upland downs and seaside turf composed mainly of species of *Festuca* and *Agrostis* contributed largely to the ascendancy of particular districts in various branches of sport. Kent enjoyed cricket supremacy early in the eighteenth century through the abundance of short, close turf on the open downs of the inner weald.

While sport was pursuing its advance, gardening was also developing and we read that during the Commonwealth 'gardening is practised for food's sake in a kitchen-garden and orchard or for pleasure's sake in a green grass plot and an arbor'.

The royal gardens, greatly extended by Charles II, saw further changes during Queen Anne's reign when she ordered that the *parterre* before the great terrace at Windsor should be turfed. Queen Caroline, Consort of George II, enlarged and planted Kensington Gardens and from Lord Walpole's correspondence we learn that she planned to close St. James's Park and to convert it into a garden for the palace. On asking an adviser what it might cost, she was told: 'Only three crowns.'

Gardening design underwent a very sweeping change of style early in the eighteenth century. From rigid formality, with vegetable sculpture and statuary in abundance, the fashion changed to a more natural style of landscape gardening. The lawn really came into its own, with broad expanses of sweeping undulating turf in front of the large houses which were being built at that time; and gardening literature of the period records the quickening interest in lawns, and seeds mixtures for their formation.

Verdant expanses of turf need mowing and the invention of the rotary mowing-machine by Edwin Budding in 1830 is an all-important milestone in lawn history. Budding, a foreman in a textile factory, adapted the principle of a machine used for shearing the nap from cloth and, according to the original patent specification, was of the opinion that

'Country gentlemen will find in using my machine an amusing useful and healthful exercise.'

Heuer[1] makes a most interesting contribution to the history of the development of the lawnmower. We learn that Ransomes began to manufacture mowers in 1832, obtaining a licence from Budding to make machines according to his patent and one of their earliest machines was presented to the Science Museum, Kensington, some years ago.

William Cobbett in *The English Garden*, 1838, does not appear to have heard of Budding's invention, for in praise of the scythe he writes:

'A good short grass mower is a really able-workman and if the plat have a good bottom, he will leave it very nearly as smooth and even as the piece of green cloth which covers the table on which I am writing: it is surprising how close a scythe will go if in a hand that knows how to whet it and use it.'

Shanks patented the first horse-machine in 1842 and Greens their chair-driven 'Silens Messor' in 1859.

The first departure from the standard design came in 1869 when

---

[1] Heuer, F. J.: *The Mechanics of Horticulture*. South Africa Institute of Park Administration.

Fellows & Bate of Manchester patented the side-wheel mower, and a further innovation of this type was the Pennsylvania machine patented in 1878. The Summers Patent machine, driven by steam power, was introduced by Leylands in 1893 and Greens brought out a steam-driven mower with seat and steering gear a little later.

The first petrol-driven mower was produced by Ransomes in 1902, and an innovation of considerable importance was the gang-mower patented by Worthington, of Shawnee, U.S.A., in 1914.

Thus we pass through the ages to the lawns and sports grounds of to-day. Beale[1] describes the part played by British seedsmen when the country caught the 'golfing fever' early in this century and his account of the establishment, from seeds, of many of the well-known inland courses makes most interesting reading.

It must never be forgotten that these pioneers prescribed the original seeds mixtures and established rates of sowing, when upon their knowledge depended the success or failure of golf course evolution.

Research into lawn and sports ground problems has been carried out by the leading seedsmen for very many years, but in 1929 the Board of Greenkeeping Research founded its Research Station at Bingley, in Yorkshire. The venture, financed by golf and sports clubs, is worthy of wider public support, for through its *Journal* are made known the results of critical investigation into all phases of fine turf production and management.

---

[1] Beale, R.: *Lawns for Sports.*

Chapter Two

The Lawn Grasses

Natural Order Gramineae

≫≫≫≫ ◦ ≪≪≪≪

Characteristics of the Order

Grasses are distributed universally, dominating the flora wherever conditions are favourable.

ROOTS

When seeds are sown, roots emerge; they are few in number and shortlived, but later the permanent thin fibrous roots are formed just below the surface—a factor of great importance in turf management as it allows the plant to be fed by top dressing.

STEMS

Botanists call these 'culms'. They are cylindrical, usually hollow except at the nodes, and grow from the axils of the lowermost leaves. When germination takes place the 'plumule' or first shoot forms buds at its base from which further shoots called 'tillers' are produced. The power to 'tiller' or 'tillering' is a process of great importance in lawn grasses which have to withstand close cutting for, in spite of constant defoliation, the plant increases the number of its shoots and so clothes the ground.

Generally these buds break through the enclosing leaf sheaths and are termed 'extravaginal' when they grow horizontally and 'intravaginal' when they grow up between the leaf sheaths and the stem emerging near the 'ligule'. Examples of 'extravaginal' branching are found in many members of the *genus Agrostis* (the bents) where large areas are colonized by means of overground stems or stolons.

When the branches are 'intravaginal' the plant is tufted. Chewings fescue is a good example.

18

LEAVES

In identifying grasses, the leaf exhibits characters which are of great assistance, but there are two sets of leaves. Those which grow from the roots are known as 'radical' and those which are borne by the stems 'cauline'. There are also differences in their construction which may prove confusing, for botanical descriptions usually refer to the 'radical' and not the 'cauline' leaves.

The leaf is in two parts, a lower portion which surrounds the stem called the 'sheath' and the upper portion, the leaf blade or 'lamina'. The sheath differs in form and colour, providing a useful aid to identification. In cocksfoot and some of the meadow-grasses, it forms a completely closed tube, but more often it surrounds the stem and is split from top to bottom with the margins overlapping.

The leaf blade is generally long, narrow and flat, but there is considerable variation. It is sometimes bristled and more often folded or rolled in grasses which are found in dry places.

At the point where the blade joins the sheath, a delicate membraneous outgrowth will be found, which is termed the 'ligule'. This varies in length in different species. Near the ligule the sides of the leaf sometimes terminate in claw-like projections known as 'auricles'.

INFLORESCENCE

The collection of flowers, or 'inflorescence', is commonly called the 'ear', and its parts are readily distinguishable. There is a central axis known as a 'rachis' supporting lateral stalks which bear 'spikelets'. On examination, the 'spikelet' is seen to consist of an axis, the 'rachilla', upon which is arranged a series of sessile bracts in two alternate rows. The flowers themselves are inconspicuous, being enclosed by chaffy structures called 'bracts', and flowers and 'bracts' are referred to as 'flowering glumes'. Attached to a minute stalk a little higher up than the 'sterile glumes' are another pair unequal in size, smaller, and more delicate than the empty glumes. The larger of these is known as the 'lemma', and the smaller, the 'palea'. It is between these two that the real flowers will be found.

The number of flowers in each 'spikelet' varies. Among lawn grasses the bents (*Agrostis spp.*) have only one flower, whilst the fescues (*Festuca spp.*) have several.

Whilst all our grasses have their flowers in spikelets, these must not be regarded as the whole of the inflorescence, but only part of it. The form of inflorescence already described is known as a 'panicle' but there are other forms, and in rye-grass the 'spikelets' are attached to the main axis without intervening stalks and is termed a 'spike'. When 'spikelets' are borne on short branches and the ears more closely resemble a 'spike' than a 'panicle' they are called 'false spikes' or 'spike-like panicles'. Examples are found in timothy and meadow-foxtail.

FLOWERS

It is not easy to dissect and examine a flower, and to most gardeners and greenkeepers the necessity seldom arises, but to complete the picture of this most interesting order, a brief description may prove of interest.

There are three stamens (the male parts) and one carpel (the female). The filaments of the stamens are long and slender, and attached to the middle of the anthers.

The gynaeceum consists of a single carpel with an ovary surmounted by two brush-like styles. Cross-fertilization and self-fertilization take place.

SEEDS

The seeds purchased from seedsmen are not strictly speaking true seeds, but fruits. In many cases, they will be found to consist of a considerable part of the 'spikelet' as well. Great variation occurs in shape and size so that with experience the gardener, groundsman, and greenkeeper can identify the various families represented in a seeds mixture.

The Fescue Family (*Genus Festuca*)

This is a most useful family, the fine-leaved species being included in most prescriptions of lawn grass seeds for the production of high-quality turf. Fescues are very tolerant of drought and prefer the lighter soils.

There are two distinct classes or groups of fescues:
(a) The narrow, bristle or prickle-leaved species.
(b) The broad-leaved species.

While the broad-leaved types are included in agricultural grass seed mixtures, they are of little value for lawns. A great deal of experience is needed to distinguish the many species, and fescues are often confused with wavy hair-grass (*Deschampsia flexuosa*) and moor mat grass (*Nardus stricta*).

In wavy hair-grass the leaves are folded, but a prominent ligule is present, whereas the fescues are noted for the absence or reduction of this white membranous outgrowth at the junction of the leaf blade and the sheath. When in flower, wavy hair-grass has white silky hairs at the base of the seeds, and the awn is twisted.

THE LAWN GRASSES

Moor mat grass can be distinguished by its cord-like roots and the inflorescence is a spike with all the spikelets twisted to one side.

For turf formation the following fine-leaved fescues are of commercial importance:

(1) Chewing's fescue.
(2) Genuine Red fescue.
(3) Hard fescue.
(4) Sheep's fescue.

SHEEP'S FESCUE

CHEWING'S FESCUE (*Festuca rubra*, Linn; sub-species, *fallax*, *Thuill*). Seeds per pound—486,400 approximately.

DESCRIPTION. This is a tufted red fescue often confused with sheep's fescue, but distinguished by its closed sheaths, whereas the sheath of sheep's fescue is split.

Its tufted non-creeping habit differs from the creeping lax growth of genuine red fescue.

ORIGIN OF COMMERCIAL SEED SUPPLIES. More than twelve thousand acres are grown and harvested in New Zealand. In 1945 the production was 1,100 tons, valued £325,829 (New Zealand pounds).

This species is not indigenous, having been introduced in seeds mixture which originated from an English seed-house. It was grown and marketed by a Mr. Chewing from whom the Chewing's fescue received its name.

USE AS LAWN GRASS. Chewing's fescue is one of the most popular grasses for fine turf mixtures. Putting and bowling green prescriptions

21

are normally composed of this species and New Zealand brown top (*Agrostis tenuis*).

It should not as a general rule be sown alone for although the turf formed is drought resisting and of a good colour, it is not always persistent.

A serious shortcoming was the appreciable loss in germination following shipment from New Zealand but the seeds are now kiln dried prior to shipment and of high vitality.

GENUINE RED FESCUE (*Festuca rubra*, Linn ; sub-species, *genuina vars*). Seeds per pound—450,000 approximately.

DESCRIPTION. The botanist recognizes several varieties of genuine red fescue but the essential differences are of little importance to the gardener and greenkeeper. The leaf blades are bristle-shaped resembling those of hard fescue, but the plant differs from hard, fine-leaved sheep's, and Chewing's fescue, by its creeping habit with a series of small tufts growing at intervals from the underground stems or rhizomes.

The colour is variable from light to dark green. The basal sheaths are red or pink and the flowering head is a panicle. The seeds have awns and are about the same size as hard fescue.

ORIGIN OF COMMERCIAL SEED SUPPLIES. Germany, Hungary and Denmark are producing centres. In Germany a strain of creeping red fescue is known as 'Steinach', and prior to the late war a very fine strain was raised and distributed by the Board of Greenkeeping Research. Aberystwyth S.59 also shows considerable promise as a lawn grass.

USE AS A LAWN GRASS. Red fescue is drought resisting, hard wearing and prostrate in habit, but owing to its rather lax growth, it is advisable to sow it with one of the bents for the formation of compact turf.

Seedsmen use this valuable grass extensively as a component of prescriptions for putting and bowling greens.

Great opportunities exist for further selection, particularly from the varieties which are found in sea-washed turf, for ordinary commercial strains vary considerably.

HARD FESCUE (*Festuca longifolia*, Thuill) syn. *F. ovina* var. *duriuscula*. Seeds per pound—470,000 approximately.

DESCRIPTION. To seedsmen this grass is known as *Festuca ovina* var. *duriuscula*, but it would appear that *F. longifolia* is the correct description. As compared with other fescues, the leaf blade is coarse and while the basal leaves are bristle-like, the stem leaves are flat and open. The seeds are twice the size of fine leaved sheep's fescue, and bear awns.

ORIGIN OF COMMERCIAL SEED SUPPLIES. Substantial quantities are grown and harvested in Germany and Holland.

USE AS A LAWN GRASS. Owing to its comparatively coarse leaf blade, hard fescue is not included in the highest-quality mixtures but it is a useful species for cricket outfields, golf fairways, football grounds, and owing to its power of resisting drought, usually an ingredient of prescriptions for tee-ing grounds on golf courses. Seeds are of good quality and usually retain their vitality.

SHEEP'S FESCUE (*Festuca ovina*. Linn). Seeds per pound— 470,000 approximately.

DESCRIPTION. An indigenous species of which commercial strains are variable.

The habit is tufted and dwarf, the leaves are slender but not so fine as the fine-leaved sheep's fescue. Seeds have an awn point.

ORIGIN OF COMMERCIAL SUPPLIES. Germany and Holland are main sources of supply.

USE AS A LAWN GRASS. Sheep's fescue establishes itself normally on moorland and light sandy soils, but seed supplies are low, and this limits its wider use in mixtures. Fine-leaved sheep's fescue is however superior in texture and is normally preferred.

FINE-LEAVED SHEEP'S FESCUE (*Festuca ovina tenuifolia*). Seeds per pound—1,120,000 approximately.

DESCRIPTION. The botanical name is used by the seed trade, but it would appear that its correct designation is *F. capillata*, Lam, *tenuifolia*, Sibth.

A low-growing tufted species with leaf blades which are almost hair-like, it wears well and is superior to the ordinary sheep's fescue.

The seeds are readily distinguishable from all fine-leaved fescues by the absence of an awn.

The inflorescence is a compact panicle and the flower stalk just below the flowering head is usually rough. This is an indigenous species.

ORIGIN OF COMMERCIAL SEED SUPPLIES. Germany and Holland.

USE AS A LAWN GRASS. Fine-leaved sheep's fescue is drought resistant and establishes itself upon most soils except those which are wet and heavy. It should not be sown alone to produce the finest quality turf,

23

but as a constituent of mixtures for putting greens and high-quality lawns, it is most useful.

CUMBERLAND MARSH FESCUE (*Festuca rubra genuina* var. *glaucescens*. Hack). Seeds per pound—540,000 approximately.

DESCRIPTION. A fine-leaved uniform creeping variety of red fescue. The plant is bluish-green in colour and assumes a somewhat lax habit.

ORIGIN OF COMMERCIAL SEED SUPPLIES. Limited quantities are home produced but in the main seeds are hand gathered from the Cumberland marshes and consequently samples are very pure.

USE AS A LAWN GRASS. Blending well with brown top, this variety is rated high as a component of seeds mixtures for bowling and golf greens. In common with all strains and varieties of red fescue it is susceptible to Autumn Rust (*Corticium fuciforme*).

The Bent Family (*Genus Agrostis*)

Seeds per pound—4,500,000 approximately.

It is unfortunate that the hard-flowering stems of perennial rye-grass and crested dogstail are referred to as 'bents' for the real bent-grasses, species of *Agrostis*, are rated highly as constituents of mixtures for lawns, bowling and putting greens.

BENT-GRASS

From this family we may develop our ideal lawn grass which sown alone will produce the perfect lawn; time will tell. In the meantime, there are many fine species, which in conjunction with the fescues are capable of producing our finest turf.

24

THE LAWN GRASSES

The bents are small-leaved and slow-growing grasses readily recognized when in flower by their delicate spreading flowering heads with small one-flowered spikelets.

Efforts are being made to clear up the confusion which exists in the nomenclature and classification of the members of the family, for at the present time some species are known by many different names. Uniformity would assist the scientist and the seedsman and enable the student to gather knowledge far more quickly than he can to-day.

NEW ZEALAND BROWN TOP (*Agrostis tenuis* Sibth. Syn. *Agrostis vulgaris*, Linn).

DESCRIPTION. A tufted perennial with underground creeping stems, but while most species are noted for their creeping habit *A. tenuis* creeps less extensively.

Finely ribbed, short leaves, tapering to a point. There is a short blunt ligule.

Inflorescence, a panicle, delicately branched, usually purple. Seeds awnless, but one variety produces seeds with the awn present.

ORIGIN OF COMMERCIAL SEED SUPPLIES. Large quantities are exported each season from New Zealand, but the species is not indigenous, having been brought by settlers, who filled their mattresses with grass prior to setting sail.

On arrival, they emptied their bedding and brown top succeeded in establishing itself.

German mixed bent also contains a proportion of brown top.

USE AS A LAWN GRASS. New Zealand brown top is a very popular grass included in most prescriptions for putting and bowling greens. The seeds are exceedingly light and should never be sown deeply but merely covered with fine soil. The turf formed is of good colour and texture. It wears well and can be sown alone or as part of a mixture.

The very many strains which exist provide excellent material for selection.

MARITIME CREEPING BENT (*Agrostis stolonifera*, Linn, var. *maritima*).

DESCRIPTION. This is not a species but a variety. The leaves are small, thin and pointed, with ribs not well defined. Ligule, long and pointed.

Inflorescence a panicle which becomes more compact after flowering. Seeds awnless.

ORIGIN OF COMMERCIAL SEED SUPPLIES. This variety is found in sea-washed turf and has been selected. Supplies are usually home produced.

USE AS A LAWN GRASS. Sown alone, it forms a compact turf of the finest quality, and it is a valuable component of prescriptions for putting greens.

VELVET BENT (*Agrostis, canina*, Linn.).

DESCRIPTION. A species with leafy trailing shoots, which enable one plant to form a mat over a comparatively large area.

Leaves fine and almost needle-like. Ligule long, tapering and pointed, a valuable aid to the identification of the species.

Inflorescence a panicle. Flowers green or purplish. The inflorescence provides a further clue to identification, as there is a strong awn to the fertile glume.

ORIGIN OF COMMERCIAL SEED SUPPLIES. This species is grown in the United States of America and Canada.

USE AS A LAWN GRASS. Sown alone it forms a springy compact turf of good colour. At one time it was regarded as the 'queen of putting green grasses'. There are many strains, but those which are available in commercial quantities appear to possess loose overground runners or stolons, liable to be torn when the turf is mown, creating an uneven surface. It should however be emphasized that these commercial strains are usually impure, and without further selection the species should not be under-rated.

REDTOP OR FIORIN (*Agrostis stolonifera*, Linn. var. *gigantea*, Koch).

Trade names which are synonymous: *Agrostis alba*, Linn.; *Agrostis palustris*, Hudson; *Agrostis nigra*, Withering; *Agrostis stolonifera* var. major. Malte.

DESCRIPTION. White scaly rhizomes enable the grass to creep, forming a coarse loose sward. When grown in isolation, a single plant makes tufts 1 to 2 feet in diameter, varying in height from $2\frac{1}{2}$ to 3 feet or more. The vigorous root stalks are shallow and generally 2 to 6 inches in length.

The leaves are short, generally broad and tapering to a point. The ligule is long and rounded at the top. The inflorescence is a panicle which tends to close up after flowering.

ORIGIN OF COMMERCIAL SEED SUPPLIES. Redtop ranks second in

importance as a pasture grass in the United States of America and about 85 per cent of the world's supply of seed is produced in a dozen counties in southern Illinois, having been produced there since 1875.

The concentration of redtop seed production in southern Illinois is due to a combination of factors, favourable climate, and soils not well adapted to other crops.

USE AS A LAWN GRASS. This is not a high-class lawn grass and is not included in prescriptions to form turf of the first quality. It is, however, frequently a component of the cheaper mixtures.

FIORIN   SMOOTH-STALKED MEADOW-GRASS

The Meadow-Grass Family (*Genus Poa*)

Annual meadow-grass is well known as a weed of fine turf but there are three species which are used extensively in mixtures for lawns and sports grounds.

(1) Smooth-stalked Meadow-Grass (*Poa pratensis*, Linn.).
(2) Rough-stalked Meadow-Grass (*Poa trivialis*, Linn.).
(3) Wood Meadow-Grass (*Poa nemoralis*, Linn.).

The meadow-grasses are not used for the production of the finest dwarf sward, but they are useful ingredients of prescriptions intended to form what may be regarded as second-class lawns.

SMOOTH-STALKED MEADOW-GRASS (*Poa pratensis*, Linn.)
Seeds per pound—1,800,000 approximately.

DESCRIPTION. A perennial with well-developed whitish creeping rhizomes and smooth stems above ground. The ligules are short and blunt. Leaves folded in the shoot and the shoots are flattened.

Inflorescence a panicle with compressed spikelets. Seeds strongly keeled and triangular in cross section with a tiny mop of soft hairs at the base. There are three or four seeds in each spikelet. In well-cleaned samples, the web of hairs is usually absent.

ORIGIN OF COMMERCIAL SEED SUPPLIES. In the United States of America, this is known as Kentucky Blue Grass and the U.S.A. is our chief source of supply.

USE AS A LAWN GRASS. While not used for putting or bowling greens and other fine turf, it is very useful for recreation grounds, cricket outfields, football and hockey grounds, golf fairways, teeing grounds, and in fact all turf subjected to hard wear. Smooth-stalked meadow-grass can withstand treading, recovering rapidly. Preferring the drier types of soils, smooth-stalked meadow-grass grows slowly in the early stages, but when established, it is one of the earliest to commence growth in the spring. It should not be sown alone, but as part of a mixture.

ROUGH-STALKED MEADOW-GRASS (*Poa trivialis*, Linn.)
Seeds per pound—2,000,000 approximately.

DESCRIPTION.This grass closely resembles the preceding species, but it does not produce long rhizomes and whilst it creeps to a limited extent, the rhizomes are small and thin. The stems are somewhat narrower than those of the smooth-stalked meadow-grass and taper to a point. Inflorescence, a panicle with spreading branches. Seeds triangular in cross section, pointed at the apex and in uncleaned samples there is a mop of hairs at the base.

ORIGIN OF COMMERCIAL SEED SUPPLIES. Denmark exports appreciable quantities to the British market.

USE AS A LAWN GRASS. Used chiefly as a constituent for second-class lawns. It is less hardy than smooth-stalked meadow-grass, suffering more readily from frost and drought, and does not wear well. It prefers a moist soil and does not start growth so early in the spring. On dry land, it becomes dwarfed and the foliage turns red.

A great disadvantage is its habit of producing unsightly overground creeping shoots, which, when removed by the mower, result in bare patches.

Rough-stalked meadow-grass should not be sown alone.

WOOD MEADOW-GRASS (*Poa nemoralis*, Linn.). Seeds per pound—2,500,000 approximately.

DESCRIPTION. A tufted or occasionally slightly creeping perennial. Weaker and more slender than the last two species. Leaves dark green, narrow and limp. Inflorescence a panicle contracted or spreading loosely. Spikelets with two to five seeds in each. Tuft of hairs present at base of each seed when sample has not been cleaned.

ORIGIN OF COMMERCIAL SEED SUPPLIES. The bulk of our supplies, although imports are not heavy as compared with the preceding species, comes from Germany and Holland.

USE AS A LAWN GRASS. For mixtures of grasses for shaded and enclosed places, this species is of great value and forms the basis of all good prescriptions. Would appear also to be a species for inclusion in mixtures for golf teeing grounds.

ROUGH-STALKED MEADOW-GRASS   WOOD MEADOW-GRASS

The Dog's-Tail Family (*Genus Cynosurus*)

The genus is made up of two British and one Mediterranean species, but of the two native species, *C. cristatus* and *C. echinatus*, the former perennial and the latter annual, only *C. cristatus* interests us.

CRESTED DOG'S-TAIL (*Cynosurus cristatus*, Linn.). Seeds per pound—862,000 approximately.

DESCRIPTION. A tufted grass, with short narrow leaves which are dark green, and have a tendency to spread sideways. Flowering head a spike-like panicle with the spikelets turned to one side of the head. Three to five flowers in each fertile spikelet. Seeds uniform in size, yellow to deep brown, terminating in a short point.

CRESTED DOG'S-TAIL   TIMOTHY

ORIGIN OF COMMERCIAL SEED SUPPLIES. New Zealand, Northern Ireland and Holland.

USE AS A LAWN GRASS. This species is drought resistant and succeeds upon a variety of soils, but should not be included in mixtures for putting and bowling greens. For cricket outfields, and football grounds, it is, however, of great value.

An objection is the formation of dry hard stalks which survive mowing when this is not regular and which tend to disfigure the sward. Like perennial rye-grass, these stems are also often referred to as 'bents' in many parts of the country.

The Cat's-Tail Family (*Genus Phleum*)

A small genus of which one species, *Phleum pratense*, is useful for lawn turf.

TIMOTHY (*Phleum pratense*, Linn.). Seeds per pound—1,200,000 approximately.

DESCRIPTION. Growing generally in tufts. The leaves rather soft but rough at the edges. Panicles cylindrical and spike-like. Outer glumes boat shaped with short stiff point or awn. Flowering glumes shorter, very thin with short stiff point or awn. Often mistaken for meadow-foxtail but is a much later grass rarely flowering until the spikelets of meadow-foxtail have fallen.

ORIGIN OF COMMERCIAL SEED SUPPLIES. This species owes its common name to Timothy Hanson who was responsible for its introduction in the U.S.A. Canada and America are producing centres. S.50 is home-produced.

USE AS A LAWN GRASS. Regaining popularity, especially when extensive turf areas are to be sown on heavy clay soil. On thin dry soils the lower nodes upon the stem become thickened and an open thin plant is produced.

The Aberystwyth strain S.50 offers possibilities for the wider use of timothy, for this strain has a multi-tillering habit and possesses marked powers of recovery under conditions of close mowing.

The Rye-Grass Family (*Genus Lolium*)

For the production of pastures and leys, perennial rye-grass (*Lolium perenne*, Linn.) and Italian rye-grass (*Lolium italicum*, Braun) are held in high esteem by agriculturists. The latter is a cultivated variety of the perennial rye-grass, but it is used very little for lawn purposes for it is only of short duration, persisting not more than two years.

Perennial rye-grass included in most prescriptions where fine turf is not desired is offered by seedsmen under various names such as Pacey's rye-grass and fine-leaved rye-grass, but these do not represent varieties, but are names used in the seed trade to describe seeds of certain sizes and weights. For instance, the smaller or 'short seeded' forms passing through a comparatively fine sieve, usually produce young plants with thin leaves. Thus, small seeds showing a heavier weight per bushel are often given the name 'Pacey perennial'. Commercial strains of perennial rye-grass are variable in texture and durability, but the introduction of indigenous leafy strains has improved this grass for lawn purposes.

PERENNIAL RYE-GRASS (*Lolium perenne*, Linn.). Seeds per pound—225,000 approximately.

DESCRIPTION. An erect tufted grass. The young shoots are flattened with the leaves folded in the shoot, but the shoots of older leaves tend to become more round. Leaf blades smooth and dark green. Ligule is extremely short and there are claw-like appendages or auricles which clasp the stem.

Inflorescence a spike; with one spikelet at each notch of the rachis and alternating in two opposite rows with the backs of the seeds towards the rachis. The seeds are described as 'canoe shaped' and are awnless.

PERENNIAL RYE-GRASS   WAVY HAIR-GRASS

ORIGIN OF COMMERCIAL SEED SUPPLIES. Ireland, Scotland, England, New Zealand, U.S.A., and Australia.

USE AS A LAWN GRASS. A leafy strain of perennial rye-grass is a useful ingredient of mixtures for sports fields and recreation grounds and often forms the bulk of mixtures for second-class garden lawns where fine turf is not desired.

For turf production upon football and hockey pitches this grass is of high value for few grasses can withstand treading during the winter months, but perennial rye-grass is an exception. The Aberystwyth strains S.23 and S.101 are preferred.

1a.　A weed-infested sward

1b.　The same sward treated with selective weed-killer

2a. Commercial strain of Timothy

2b. Leafy strain of Timothy

The Hair-Grass Family (*Deschampsia* and *Aira*)

While these grasses are of little value for agricultural purposes several species grow abundantly upon heaths and moorland and the wavy hair-grass (*Deschampsia flexuosa*, Trin.) is found upon fairways and on the 'rough' of many golf courses, constructed upon moorland or heathland soils.

WAVY HAIR-GRASS (*Deschampsia flexuosa*, Trin—*Aira flexuosa*, Linn.).

DESCRIPTION. To seedsmen this grass is usually known as *Aira flexuosa*, but its correct botanical name is *Deschampsia flexuosa*.

The leaves are narrow with the edges tightly rolled inwards, dark green in colour, but often with pinkish bases.

The ligule is short and broad with the apex blunt; auricles are absent.

The inflorescence is an erect and spreading panicle with two spikelets and a rudimentary third. The fertile glume has a twisted awn extending beyond its apex.

ORIGIN OF COMMERCIAL SEED SUPPLIES. Germany.

USE AS A LAWN GRASS. Wavy hair-grass has a limited use and should never be included in prescriptions to form first-class turf. However, upon acid moorland and heaths for golf courses and sports grounds it is often an ingredient of the mixture. It can also establish itself in shaded and enclosed positions, providing soil conditions are favourable.

Commercial seed samples are as a rule not of high quality and when purchasing, the germination of the sample should be asked for, as well as a statement of its purity. Seedsmen will be happy to furnish this information.

For fairways of golf courses on acid soils this species has a great deal to recommend it, for the texture is fine and the colour good.

Re-selection will do much to improve and probably enhance the popularity of this grass.

TUFTED HAIR-GRASS (*Deschampsia caespitosa*, Beauv.; *Aira caespitosa*, Linn.).

DESCRIPTION. Leaves inclined to be coarse and ribbed, with the margins of the leaf blades scabrid. The sheath is split with the shoots oval or compressed.

Ligule white, very long, acute and often bifid. Auricles are absent.

C   33

Inflorescence a graceful spreading panicle.

Spikelets, numerous, containing two flowers and a rudimentary third. Fertile glume with sub-dorsal awn.

ORIGIN OF COMMERCIAL SEED SUPPLIES. Not obtainable in commercial quantities.

USE AS A LAWN GRASS. There appears little use at present for this species either for lawn or agricultural purposes, but there is wide variation in the strains found growing wild and a much improved type may be developed.

Golf courses can use it as a hazard on inland in much the same way as marram-grass is used on seaside courses. Clumps of the grass make most fearsome-looking obstacles planted in the sand at the base of the bunkers.

TUFTED HAIR-GRASS

Chapter Three

Seeds Mixtures

❧❧❧❧ ◦ ❧❧❧❧

Good lawns have been produced by sowing a single species but the limitations of many grasses and the variation in the habit of commercial strains make it desirable to compound species into prescriptions or mixtures.

An anonymous author[1] writing early in the eighteenth century discourages the use of 'hay seeds' and advises that seeds for lawns should be gathered from 'the grass of clean upland pastures'. A description of the grasses employed for the production of lawns and sports turf illustrates that the most valuable species are those which can withstand the punishing effects of mowing, establish themselves upon a variety of soils, have a marked degree of persistency and possess a capacity for tillering or side-shoot production. These qualities will be found in the grasses of the upland sheep pasture, the species which, under natural conditions, occur on the poorer soils.

Providing the seedsman knows the nature of the soil and the condition of the seed bed, a mixture can be recommended for the type of sward required.

Our present knowledge of their performance under conditions of close mowing and the variability of commercial strains renders, with certain exceptions, the adoption of a single species for lawn making extremely hazardous, accordingly two, three, four, or more species are combined to form a mixture.

Too long has an agricultural bias influenced the decisions of those whose business it is to compile mixtures. Lawn seed prescriptions have evolved from hay loft sweepings, through a phase of what may be termed the multi-species, hit or miss mixture until, to-day, we stand at the cross-roads. Our knowledge of the performance of the various grasses under conditions of close mowing, although imperfect, has advanced and although we may desire a limitation in the number of species forming a

[1] Rohde, Eleanor Sinclair: *Nineteenth Century and After*.

35

mixture, cost is often a deciding factor. Those who sow lawns and sports turf must bear in mind that a sward composed of dense, low-growing grasses may present a higher initial cost, yet the preponderance of rapid-growing agricultural species in a lower-priced mixture will later bring increased maintenance charges.

An advance to more simple mixtures can only be brought about by the inclusion of pedigree leafy strains of proved reliability and by the further selection of new strains.

For the production of the finest turf for putting and bowling greens it is possible to restrict the species to two, and a mixture of

> *By weight*
> 70 per cent Chewing's fescue
> 30 per cent Brown top

is regarded as a standard prescription. We depend however upon importation for our supplies of these useful species and when through economic or other causes it is necessary to use stocks sparingly owing to restricted imports the proportion of brown top is reduced as follows:

> *By weight*
> 90 per cent Chewing's fescue
> 10 per cent Brown top

This mixture, retailing at approximately 7s. per pound, represents excellent value but the possibility of the periodic disappearance of brown top from the market is disquieting, for Chewing's fescue sown alone has not a sufficiently high performance to make possible its recommendation. The Aberystwyth strain S.59 red fescue is the alternative but supplies of this home-produced strain are at present limited. In the absence of brown top, S.59 is preferred to Chewing's for the latter does not colonize itself by creeping, whereas S.59 creeps extensively, withstands close cutting and maintains a good winter colour. S.59 is not advocated as an exception to the rule that two, three or more species should form a mixture for the production of lawn turf but should brown top become unavailable there are few alternatives.

While the suitability of the grasses chosen to produce the best sward for a particular purpose should be the guiding principle in the compilation of a prescription, seedsmen are often called upon to prepare mixtures without rye-grass to meet the demand of the retail lawn seed trade. Such mixtures, however, must be sold at a competitive price—usually in the region of 5s. per pound. In the circumstances, additions must be made to the more simple formula of Chewing's fescue and brown top, and crested dogstail, smooth-stalked meadow-grass, rough-stalked meadow-grass and fiorin have, in the past, been called into service.

Smooth-stalked meadow-grass and fiorin are, however, products of a hard currency area—America—and their importation is prohibited. What may be termed the lower-grade non-rye-grass mixture must therefore be formed from varying proportions of Chewing's fescue, brown top, crested dogstail, and rough-stalked meadow-grass. The last, unfortunately, has many shortcomings for while it is finer-leaved than smooth-stalked, it produces surface creeping runners which are often removed by mowing, leaving a thin sward. It is, however, a useful 'nurse' grass, protecting slower-growing grasses in a seedling sward, and establishes itself rapidly upon soils retaining moisture.

Crested dogstail is a hardwearing species forming a low-growing, dense sward on a variety of soils but it does not creep and the leaf blade is less fine than Chewing's fescue and brown top.

Smooth-stalked meadow-grass is sadly missed from the market for this species is remarkably hardwearing and colonizes rapidly by means of underground stems or rhizomes. Fiorin or red top is a species of no great importance, for although a species of *Agrostis*, it is not fine-leaved and produces a preponderance of stalky growths. It would appear that its chief value is the improvement in the appearance of a seeds mixture by the inclusion of a proportion of small seeds which resemble those of brown top. Until the purchasing public and those who retail lawn grass seeds are better informed and consequently more discriminating, seedsmen will be called upon to present a 'fine-looking, low-priced mixture', particularly when fiorin returns to the market. Sales can be lost upon the appearance of a sample and a mixture containing S.23 perennial rye-grass will probably find less favour owing to the presence of the larger seeds, yet upon all counts this compact, prostrate, leafy strain is more desirable than the minute-seeded but stalky fiorin.

The following are therefore suggested for this type of mixture.

By weight
50 per cent Crested dogstail
40 per cent Chewing's fescue
10 per cent Brown top

or *By weight*
40 per cent Crested dogstail
40 per cent Chewing's fescue
10 per cent Brown top
10 per cent Timothy

or   *By weight*
             40 per cent Crested dogstail
             40 per cent Chewing's fescue
             10 per cent Brown top
             10 per cent Rough-stalked meadow-grass

Rough-stalked meadow-grass is included for sale in districts with heavy clay and medium loam soils. The finer grasses are included in each mixture at a proportion of not less than 50 per cent, and a common practice of subjugating their proportion to low percentages is not recommended, for a mixture with 80 or 90 per cent of crested dogstail will result in a sward in which Chewing's fescue and brown top cannot compete and are usurped.

When smooth-stalked meadow-grass is available again, mixtures can be revised as follows:

          By weight
             40 per cent Chewing's fescue
             30 per cent Crested dogstail
             10 per cent Smooth-stalked meadow-grass
             10 per cent Rough-stalked meadow-grass
             10 per cent Brown top

This would prove a good general purpose mixture.

The low price of commercial perennial rye-grass has influenced the inclusion of the species in lawn mixtures and seedsmen find a ready sale for prescriptions in which this easily grown grass is included. It must be borne in mind that very many garden lawns are sown upon poor soils with inadequate preparation. Perennial rye-grass growing rapidly from seeds establishes itself quickly and appears unaffected by conditions of soil and climate under which the finer grasses would probably fail. The greenkeeper and groundsman are masters of the art of soil pre-treatment and seed-bed preparation and can be trusted to produce a satisfactory turf from the finer, but slow-growing grasses; the amateur gardener is often less knowledgeable, fails with a more costly mixture, and then in despair sows a less expensive grade. Perennial rye-grass is, without doubt, a valuable component of a mixture for recreation grounds and, with crested dogstail, should form the basis of prescriptions to form turf for winter games. Smooth-stalked meadow-grass is also a candidate with strong claims for inclusion in this mixture but until it returns a suggested mixture for football and hockey is:

SEEDS MIXTURES

By weight
> 80 per cent Perennial rye-grass
> 20 per cent Crested dogstail

Timothy S.50, a pedigree strain, will gain increased popularity for sports turf making, when its many virtues are known. This strain tillers freely and withstands mowing, but it is doubtful whether it is sufficiently hardwearing to merit inclusion in mixtures for winter games. For the golf fairway a suggested prescription is:

By weight
> 25 per cent Perennial rye-grass
> 10 per cent S.50 Timothy
> 10 per cent Crested dogstail
> 45 per cent Chewing's fescue
> 10 per cent Brown top

It will be appreciated that the suggested mixtures are made in the nature of a guide and when extensive areas are to be sown, an advisory visit by an expert should be arranged. Where prices are mentioned these are in all cases approximate and before making serious calculations buyers are advised to secure quotations from reputable seedsmen.

Chapter Four

Growing Lawn Grasses for Seeds

⪫⪫⪫⪫ ◦ ⪪⪪⪪⪪

The Production of Pedigree Strains

Seed saving is as old as civilization itself, the practice of saving seeds long being regarded as the hallmark of good husbandry.

Development produced the specialist, the seedgrower, whose broad acres were planted not with crops, for leaf or root, but for seeds.

Progress in these far-off days was made by selection, and travellers returning from foreign lands brought with them new and interesting varieties until the crops in farms and gardens bore but little resemblance to their earlier ancestors.

When Thomas Fairchild in 1717 crossed a carnation with a sweet william and produced plants intermediate in habit, this was the birth of plant breeding and the work grew apace. In 1866 Gregor Mendel published his discovery of the laws of inheritance, reducing to numerical law the recurrence of inherited characters, but his work was neglected until 1900 when it was publicized by de Vries, Tschermatk and Correns. Genetics, or the science of the gene, heralded a new era in plant breeding, providing a systematic basis.

From time to time reference is made in greenkeeping literature to the part that can be played by improved strains of lawn grasses in the perfection of lawns and sports grounds; accordingly a genetical background is not without interest to greenkeeper and groundsman.

GENES

The gene is a unit or factor of inheritance and although it is as yet unseen, research has shown that genes govern the form, growth and development of plants. That grasses should be tufted or stoloniferous, their leaf blades rough or smooth, their maturity early or late, is controlled by genes. It will thus be appreciated what an important part they play.

40

CHROMOSOMES

While we have not seen a gene, we have under the microscope observed within the active nucleus of a plant cell a number of thread-like bodies, the chromosomes. These are the 'houses' in which the genes live. The number of chromosomes is the same in each body cell of all plants of the same species, and plant growth takes place by cell division, the chromosomes splitting longitudinally. Thus a species with twenty-four chromosomes will split and form forty-eight, half the number moving to one end of the cell, half to the other, and a cell wall is formed between them. We now have two cells where there was one, the plant is growing.

The cells of the pollen grains, the male parent and the unfertilized ovule, the mother or seed-bearer, do not carry the full number of chromosomes found in the body cells, or when fertilization took place a plant with twice the number would be produced. A species with forty-eight chromosomes will have twenty-four in the male reproductive cells and an equal number in the female. When united the normal complement is restored: forty-eight, half from the male and half from the female. A plant then derives its characteristics from both parents, a factor of great importance in plant breeding.

MENDEL'S LAWS

In lawn grasses a pair of genes will control the height to which an uncut plant will grow, one gene may be responsible for plants 1 ft. in height, another may produce plants 3 ft. tall. We have therefore a dwarf gene and a tall gene and as they both control height they are referred to as related genes or allelomorphs, and are represented by capital and small letters, T for tall and tt for dwarf.

Now if a tall variety is crossed with a dwarf variety of the same species the progeny in the first generation are tall. When the plants are self-pollinated and the seeds sown, the plants produced in the next generation will be of two types, tall and dwarf, in the proportion of three tall to one dwarf. Making use of representative letters the reason is plainly seen:

```
(Tall) TT          X          tt  (Dwarf)
                Tt  (Tall)
TT              Tt          Tt              tt
```

It will be noted that TT plants carry tall genes only. Tt plants carry tall and dwarf, whilst tt plants have only dwarf genes. When seeds from self-pollinated TT plants are sown they will produce TT plants only, they can do no other, likewise tt offspring will be produced from plants of this type. The position is different however when progeny from Tt parents are examined. These plants will be divided into tall and dwarf in the same fixed proportions.

Tallness is more assertive than dwarfness and is called dominant, dwarfness is a recessive characteristic. These are the principles upon which Mendel based his laws.

PRACTICAL DEDUCTIONS

It has been shown how characteristics are inherited and how wide variation can occur. Through the ages natural cross-pollination by the agency of wind and insects has increased the genetical complication. Mutation can also occur; a plant growing in the field may fail to form a cell wall when the chromosomes divide, and cells with double their normal chromosome number may be formed. These mutants may be desirable or undesirable but a new type of plant is produced.

Grasses grown for generations and selected for the production of seeds will tend to acquire a capacity for seed production, they will become increasingly less leafy and dense. This factor was realized by Sir R. G. Stapledon and his work in the improvement of herbage strains has proved an outstanding achievement in British agriculture. Stapledon turned from the commercial stocks of grass seeds and selected plants found in various situations. Pasture strains of perennial rye-grass were bred from plants found in good old pastures. Timothy, cocksfoot, fescues and red clover also received attention from his workers at the Welsh Plant Breeding Station and excellent strains for hay and pasture were produced and grown for seed by British growers.

This work was undertaken to improve farm grasses but there is a vast uncharted field for work of a similar nature to improve strains of lawn grasses. Seedsmen are alive to the problem but it must be borne in mind that the work is costly. Pedigree strains will cost more and unless the purchaser realizes the advantages of sowing the improved grasses initial cost may be the deciding factor in buying.

Seed Growing

A large proportion of seeds of fine lawn grasses required for the home market are imported and while we grow most of our own rye-gras and smaller quantities of crested dogstail and timothy, the main centres of production are Scotland and Northern Ireland. With the exception of the Fen country where a limited quantity of rye-grass is grown, until recent years only occasional crops of grass seeds were grown in England and Wales.

It is strange that with such a favourable climate for the growth of grasses a wider selection of lawn grass seeds is not home-produced, but seed crops, cereals, roots, flowers and vegetables tend to segregate into specialized areas. Thus Chewing's fescue and brown top, although introduced into New Zealand, have become exports of great value to that country. Smooth-stalked meadow-grass or, as it is often called, Kentucky blue grass, is grown almost exclusively in the U.S.A., and hard fescue is associated with German seed growing. Specialization of this kind leaves Great Britain ill-equipped to supply seeds for turf making during the aftermath of war when currency cannot be provided for the purchase of what are regarded as luxury grasses.

The answer is an increase in seed production in this country and with the wider cultivation of the pedigree strains bred by the Welsh Plant Breeding Station a very encouraging start has been made. Although the pedigree strains raised at Aberystwyth were produced for agricultural purposes, it has already been seen that several show promise for lawn making, and have been grown by British farmers for a number of years. Supplies, however, are restricted and an increased acreage combined with further selection of strains of the more valuable grasses is called for if Great Britain is to be assured of adequate supplies independent of currency problems.

That our climate is unsuitable for grass seed production cannot be substantiated for Evans[1] informs us that grass seeds can be grown where the average rainfall is 40 inches or even more, other conditions being favourable. Commercial strains of perennial rye-grass are normally sown as a component of a mixture of grasses and clovers, are harvested once or twice for seeds, and the ley then remains as a pasture for two or three years. Average crops are 5 to 6 cwt. per acre. A comparison with the leafy pedigree pasture strain S.23 is interesting, for the average crop whether sown, broadcast, or drilled, rarely exceeds 3 to 4 cwt., which indicates a reduction in seed production when this leafy strain is grown.

Timothy grown on the coarse lands of Stirlingshire averages 3 to 5 cwt. per acre but the pedigree strain S.50 shows a reduction of 2 or 3 cwt. per acre. With good management on fertile land this crop sown in drills will produce four or five seed crops in successive seasons.

Crested dogstail grown in County Down and County Antrim produces an average seed crop of 4 to 5 cwt. per acre. As yet a pedigree

[1] Evans, Gwilym: *Herbage Seed Production.*

strain has not been developed but a more densely leafy strain is needed to supersede commercial types for turf making. Red fescue S.59 is grown in this country and average yields are 2 to 3 cwt. per acre. Four or even five crops are harvested in successive years.

The harvesting of grass seeds calls for specialized knowledge. Rye-grass growers in Ayrshire usually associate the ripening of the crop with the ripening time of blackcurrants.[1] S.23 is usually ripe a little after the middle of July. Leafy strains of timothy ripen during the latter half of August and red fescue from the end of June until early July.

The colour of the ripe heads and straw is a reliable guide to the time of harvesting and although a certain amount of the crop is lost by shedding, experienced growers limit such losses by careful handling.

In Ayrshire and Northern Ireland rye-grass is usually cut with a mower and tied into sheaves by women. The sheaves are stooked and later built into small mows. A reaper is often used, tying the sheaves by hand, but a farm binder adjusted to make narrow sheaves, with sheaf-carrier and seed-catcher attached, deals with crops effectively. During hot summer days reaping and binding during the early morning and evening minimizes losses through seed scattering.

The combine harvester is also used for crops which are dead ripe, with the exception of leafy timothy which presents difficulties and is best dealt with by the ordinary binder.

When carting a crop from the field for stacking prior to threshing, the floors of wagons are covered with canvas to collect seeds which are shed. Stooks are not untied as is the common practice with corn crops and providing the crop is well ripened and conditioned, they are loaded on to carts without untying.

Crops are threshed from the field wherever possible but when climatic conditions are unfavourable storing in sheds or barns is usual. Corn threshers are normally employed for grass seed crops, an appropriate drum speed of approximately 1,200 revolutions per minute being usual, with the wind pressure reduced.

Care is taken to ensure that damp seeds are not put into bags, the moisture content being tested by means of a moisture meter and artificial drying is resorted to when there is excessive moisture. The thorough cleaning of seed samples is of vital importance and seed merchants are equipped to deal with even the most weedy samples—cleaning them with modern machinery.

[1] *Growing Pasture Types of Grass for Seeds*. Report of the Fourth International Grassland Congress.

Chapter Five

The New Lawn

>>>>> ∘ <<<<<

A. Sowing the New Lawn

Thorough preparation and soil pre-treatment are essentials to the establishment of lawn turf and whether the area to be sown is a garden lawn of comparatively small size or a recreation ground, public park or golf fairway covering many acres the main principles are equally applicable.

GRADING AND DRAINING SPORTS FIELDS

To provide a true surface bulldozers and scrapers are employed in sports ground construction, and it is essential that when the work is completed at least four inches of fertile top-spit soil are provided to form the seed bed.

Badly drained, waterlogged soils are incapable of supporting good lawn turf, respiration vital to the well-being of plants is restricted and beneficial bacteria discouraged, when the soil is waterlogged. Making mole drains is common agricultural practice and sports turf also is drained in this way. When concrete or clay pipes are laid or mole drains made, care must be taken to provide a satisfactory outlet for the water collected in the drains.

Surface drainage by incorporating sand or 'breeze' is of great value on retentive soils.

When constructing golf fairways and public parks where a level surface is not normally essential, it is possible when grading to construct shallow depressions so arranged to lead to established ditches. Surface water is then carried away quickly after heavy rain.

GRADING AND DRAINING GARDEN LAWNS

Amateur gardeners when preparing the site for a new lawn are often perplexed over the subject of drainage, but it must be borne in mind that

45

it is not necessary in most cases to instal pipe drains, for a garden lawn cannot be compared with a bowling green where the installation of an elaborate pipe drainage system is not to ensure a good sward but to make play possible with the minimum of delay after heavy rain.

Grading is usually a hand operation, moving the soil from the higher to the lower levels, and normally a true level surface is not essential. Providing the undulations do not interfere with mowing it is unnecessary to strive laboriously to obtain a billiards-table surface unless the lawn is to be used for bowls, tennis or croquet. The wise gardener should study the site before commencing operations and strange as it may seem, the weed population will prove of great service to him, for weeds tell stories of soil deficiency or abundance, indicate that soils probably need drainage, are deficient in lime, or rich in phosphates. If comfrey, loosestrife and rushes occur then these are an indication that particular care is needed to drain the site of the lawn. Likewise chickweed grows well where phosphates are needed. Lime deficiency is shown on heavy soils by an abundance of dead nettles or wild mints. Perennial nettles more often appear on good fertile land and fat hen and sow thistles where the land is in 'good heart'. Let us then watch and record, for as there are 'sermons in stones', so also shall we find 'wisdom in weeds'.

The site for a garden lawn should be dug one 'spit' or spade-depth deep, bringing to the desired level as work proceeds. When taking out the 'footings' of new houses, builders usually bring to the surface infertile sub-soil which should be buried under the top spit. New lawns have often to be produced where previously there was meadow-land, in which case the turf should be cut and stacked prior to digging.

While the provision of pipe drainage is rarely necessary for garden lawns, where the land is likely to hold water in excess, the provision of 'weepholes' or drainage sumps is suggested. These can be dug eighteen inches or two feet square and two or three feet deep as conditions demand. The bottom six inches can be filled with hard core or large pebbles, covered with coarse clinker to within a foot of the surface. Six inches of graded clinker should then be added, followed by two inches of 'breeze' which can be obtained from the local gasworks. A tile should then be placed over the mouth of the hole and four inches of good topspit soil introduced to form a seed bed.

Where 'weepholes' are not required surface drainage can be improved by introducing a one or two-inch layer of finely sifted breeze below the top four inches of seed-bed soil. It will be noted that a minimum of four inches of top-spit soil is insisted upon for seed-bed formation and therefore if soil movement is necessary to correct marked irregularities in the surface level it is of the utmost importance that the top-spit soil should always remain upon the surface.

FALLOWING

It is a mistake to hasten sowing, for soils carry a high population of seeds of weeds and weed grasses, the destruction of which is essential to prevent weed invasion in the seedling sward. Weed inhibition at present achieved by fallowing or leaving land without a crop and cultivating to destroy successive crops of weeds as they appear, may not always be necessary in future years according to a report[1] issued following recent trials. The use of selective weed-killers is suggested, to inhibit weed growth; applications being made prior to sowing. For the purposes of these trials the site of a six-rink bowling green was divided into six trial plots, three being treated with selective weed-killers in powder form and the remaining plots acting as controls.

Plots 1, 3 and 5 were each treated with selective weed-killer at the rate of half an ounce to the square yard, and sown immediately. Plots 2, 4 and 6 were untreated prior to sowing.

The following tables summarize the results after six months.

TABLE I

A figure of 100 would represent perfect density

Plot		
1	Methoxone treated	35
2	Control	85
3	2, 4-D treated	60
4	Control	85
5	Methoxone & 2, 4-D treated	30
6	Control	85

The active ingredient either Methoxone (M.C.P.A.) or 2, 4-D (D.C.P.A.) was 1 per cent only of the powders used, the remainder being a neutral carrier but it will be noticed that a reduction in sward density resulted on the treated plots.

[1] Shirran, W., and Reed, F. J.: *Selective Herbicides; Parks, Golf Courses and Sports Grounds.*

The following table illustrates the degree of weed suppression.

TABLE II

Plot			per sq. yard
1	Methoxone treated	(a) Seedling weeds	2
		(b) Vegetative weeds	3
2	Control	(a)	18
		(b)	6
3	2, 4-D treated	(a)	2
		(b)	3
4	Control	(a)	20
		(b)	7
5	Methoxone &	(a)	3
	2, 4-D treated	(b)	4
6	Control	(a)	24
		(b)	7

The term 'vegetative' is applied to weeds produced from roots, etc., left in the soil prior to sowing.

The practical deductions to be drawn from this trial are that weed inhibition can be achieved by pre-treating with selective weed-killers, but at the expense of seedling sward density. It must be borne in mind, however, that the use of these herbicides is in a very early stage of development, but it will be appreciated that if the time taken by fallowing could be reduced and a high degree of weed control obtained by the use of selective weed-killers the problem of producing a weed-free seedling sward would be simplified.

Until more definite results are available, fallowing or planting a 'smother' crop such as potatoes will no doubt be relied upon. Thus if soil preparation is commenced in the early spring, sowing should be deferred until the autumn or in cases of severe weed infestation until the following spring. On a golf course in Cornwall it was decided to reinstate fairways which had been used for food production during the late war. The land was prepared for planting early potatoes and cultivated thoroughly.

After planting and when the crop was lifted, cultivation continued in preparation for autumn sowing with lawn grass seeds. Ploughing was followed by harrowing and then the land was rolled. Harrowing was repeated on several occasions and at the time of the final harrowing fertilizers were applied. The land was rolled again and consolidated to such an extent that a motor-car could be driven over the site without showing excessive wheel marking.

3a. Leafy perennial rye-grass growing for seed

3b. Seed crop cut and stooked

4b. Red Clover

4a. Figwort

Seeds were sown by 'fiddle' seeder, lightly harrowed and then rolled again, the sward established was comparatively weed free and the potato crop brought a good financial return.

The provision of a weed-free condition is of great importance and many failures to establish lawn turf from seeds can be traced to sowing without fallowing or adequate preparation. A bowling green in Northamptonshire was sown without a fallow and although the grasses germinated freely they were usurped by wild white clover. An inspection of adjoining grassland revealed that conditions appeared to favour the development of this weed of sports turf for it was a common and valuable component of the local pastures. Correct treatment prior to sowing would have resulted in a weed-free sward being formed at an earlier date.

When fallowing the site of a garden lawn it is a good plan to encourage the germination of seeds of weeds and weed grasses, accordingly, during dry weather, a sprinkler should be brought into use to water the soil and to germinate successive crops of weeds, hoeing them off when small.

The sprinkler can be moved as required, treating the whole of the site.

SEED-BED PREPARATION AND PRE-TREATMENT

Following a cultivated fallow the soil will be ploughed or dug and worked to a fine tilth by harrowing or hoeing. For worm destruction lead arsenate broadcast at the rate of two ounces to the square yard and incorporated with the soil is suggested, but a trial on a small area is recommended at an earlier date; for on some soils, for reasons which cannot at present be explained, lead arsenate adversely affects the germination of the seeds. It should also be borne in mind that lead arsenate is a poison and must be treated as such.

Final preparation should consist of rolling or treading followed by harrowing or raking, repeating the operations and at the final harrowing or raking an application of fertilizer should be made. Generally speaking a proprietary lawn fertilizer applied at the rate of two ounces to the square yard will give satisfactory results but for more extensive areas the following are suggested:

1 cwt. per acre sulphate of ammonia
2 cwt. per acre superphosphate
½ cwt. per acre sulphate of potash

applied by means of a fertilizer distributor. Keeble[1] records that certain lawn grasses respond by increased germination when treated with

[1] Keeble, Sir Frederick: *Science Lends a Hand in the Garden.*

othosphosphoric acid which occurs in superphosphate. Harrowing or raking will mix the fertilizers with the soil, which can then be rolled. The final condition of a seed bed for lawn grasses should resemble that of an onion bed—really firm and not showing heel marks. Whenever possible the final harrowing should take place about a fortnight before sowing for the maximum benefit will then be obtained from pre-treatment with fertilizers.

SOWING

The most opportune times for sowing are usually from the middle of March until May and from mid-August until October, but soil temperatures and conditions are of greater importance than calendar dates. Autumn sowing is preferred to spring for the soil retains summer warmth, and heavy dews encourage the growth of the grasses. Sowing in the spring is often followed by a period of prolonged dry weather and the seedling sward is handicapped in its efforts to become established. Weed invasion is also less evident during the autumn.

When seeds mixtures are delivered from the seedsman it is advisable to invert and then to shake the bags thoroughly prior to sowing, for the ingredients may have become segregated on a long journey, the fine seeds having worked to the bottom.

Sowing and cross-sowing are advised, dividing the seeds into equal parts and sowing half from north to south and half from east to west, thus the possibility of uneven distribution is minimized.

Garden lawns, cricket squares, tennis courts and bowling and golf greens are usually hand sown, but mechanical sowing is usual for golf fairways, recreation grounds, public parks and football pitches.

The 'fiddle' seeder, seeds barrow and small hand-operated fertilizer distributor are recommended, but drilling is not advised for even when cross-drilled the spaces between the rows prevent the early production of a dense sward. Whether sowing is by hand or by mechanical means the value of cross-sowing is stressed.

When reinstating golf fairways following the late war, turf establishment was hastened by under-sowing a corn crop. The seedling sward was protected by the growing cereal and after harvesting the stubble was mown out. The practice of under-sowing was resorted to in order to minimize the loss of time while a valuable food crop was grown.

Depth of sowing is important and as a general rule seeds mixtures should be sown as near to the surface as possible but with the minimum seed exposure.

Following sowing, rake and harrow lightly and then roll, but if the soil is holding moisture, refrain from rolling or seeds and soil will adhere to the roller.

SOWING RATES

Seedsmen who prescribed the early seeds mixtures established the practice of sowing at the rate of 1 to 2 oz. to the square yard for garden lawns and sports greens and from 2 to 3 cwt. per acre for more extensive areas. Of late years there has been a tendency to sow at lower rates but so many factors are involved that it is difficult to be categorical. Lewis[1] reports that on a golf course in Shropshire an additional nine holes were fit for play within ten months after sowing fairways at the remarkably low seeding rate of 79 lb. per acre and suggests that the rates could be still lower. That lower seeding rates are possible is not disputed: likewise, undoubtedly, cabbage seeds could be sown at considerably lower rates than at present employed. Figures regarding the number of seeds per pound and the probability of plants established are of great interest both to the market grower and to those who sow lawn turf but the sowing rate that can be recommended is that which in a bad season will secure an adequate 'plant' be it cabbages or seedling grasses. The success of sowing at low rates is very dependent upon a clean seed bed, but in so many cases it is necessary to sow after only a short fallow, and seeding at higher rates produces a dense sward capable of competing with aggressive weeds. Accordingly, for general-purpose sowing, these rates are recommended as standards:

1 to 2 oz. per square yard.
$1\frac{1}{2}$ to 2 cwt. per acre.

(The lower rates being suggested when the seeds mixture contains perennial rye-grass.)

THE SEEDLING SWARD

When the young grasses are about one and a half inches high the sward should be rolled and when they reach a height of from three to four inches they should be mown, or preferably scythed, for the first time. The mower blades should be set merely to top the grasses, no attempt should be made to mow closely. As growth continues cutting should be frequent with a gradual lowering of the cut and occasional rolling, but rolling when the soil is wet should be avoided or a 'capped' or 'hide-bound' surface will be formed.

[1] Lewis, I. G.: *Turf* (Faber & Faber).

STABILIZED SOIL: BITUMEN PROCESS

During war years, turf upon landing-grounds was reinforced rapidly as a result of investigations by the Alexander Asphalt Company of Bristol.

A booklet[1] describes experiments in which a proprietary bitumous peat product and a bitumen emulsion known as 'Petas' and 'Petas-ply' were used. Lawn grass seeds were sown in the normal way and then covered with 'Petas' spread at an average thickness of half an inch. Further plots were treated with the bitumen emulsion 'Petas-ply'. A layer of sharp sand was spread half an inch thick after lawn grass seed had been sown, this was sprayed with the non-toxic bitumen emulsion 'Petas-ply' and another layer of sand was applied.

The effect of bitumen treatment was to produce more rapid germination and in the case of 'Petas-ply' the mortality rate among seedling grasses was lowered. It is stated that annual weeds were largely suppressed on the treated plots. Further investigation in turf stabilization by this process appears worth while for although the cost per acre of bitumen emulsion is £56, it would appear that for golf teeing grounds, football touch lines and goal-mouth areas, the base lines of lawn tennis courts, sloping banks and roadside verges, such stabilization has distinct possibilities.

B. Turfing the New Lawn

As compared with the production of lawn turf from seeds, the laying of turves is relatively simple and if adequate supplies of good turf were available the laying of turves for garden lawns would be more often recommended.

A tennis club in East Anglia decided to reconstruct two grass courts which had deteriorated during the war years. The committee, after due consideration, decided to lay turves in preference to sowing with lawn grass seeds in order that play could be resumed with as little delay as possible. The courts were put out of play in August, stripped, and the soil prepared, turf was laid and given normal treatment, but match play was not possible the following season as the sward was composed of a mixture of desirable and very undesirable grasses, the latter asserting themselves under the improved conditions provided. Cocksfoot and

[1] Sutton, M. A. F.: *A Study of the Growth of Grass in Surface Stabilized Soil.*

52

other coarse agricultural species contributed in producing a surface upon which good club tennis could not be enjoyed and it was decided to postpone reopening the courts until the next season. Thus owing to the poor quality of the turf supplied, play for one season was lost and it would have been possible to produce a superior sward from seeds in the same time at a fraction of the cost.

For bowling greens, sea-washed turf has enjoyed enormous popularity, and to the bowler a green laid with turf from coastal sea-washed marshes is regarded as the aristocrat. It will be observed, however, that deterioration normally follows the laying of sea-washed turf until the sward bears no resemblance to that laid originally.

A parks superintendent in Middlesex made a survey of bowling greens maintained by his parks department, grading greens into three categories. His classification revealed that a number of greens formed from seeds could be included in Class 1, with sea-washed turf greens laid three years previously, while many older sea-washed greens were placed in Class 3 although they were highly rated by bowlers, purely because of the origin of the turf with which they were laid. That good turf laid after thorough preparation will produce lawns and sports greens quickly, is not disputed, but disappointment will follow laying poor meadow-turf, and valuable time can be lost.

PREPARING THE TURF BED

When preparing the seed bed for sowing lawn grass seeds fallowing to suppress weeds is recommended, and while a weed-free bed is often considered unnecessary when turves are laid, it must be borne in mind that many weeds lying dormant in the soil will penetrate the turf after laying.

A fine tilth should be well consolidated, dressed with bone meal at the rate of 2 oz. per square yard, raking the bone meal into the surface. Turf is normally supplied 3 ft. by 1 ft and $1\frac{1}{2}$ in. thick. Trials have proved that no advantage is gained by cutting turf thicker than $1\frac{1}{2}$ in.

With the introduction of selective weed-killers, turf treated with these prior to lifting is offered for sale. Needless to say, this contains less weeds than untreated samples; there is evidence, however, that turf treated in this way sometimes fails to root as freely as when untreated. No critical experimental work appears to have been carried out to ascertain whether root development is inhibited following treatment with selective weed-killers, and research along these lines is suggested. Patching carried out in late October upon the cricket table of a village club failed to knit and it was necessary to lift and relay. An examination of the lifted turves revealed a very restricted root system, and as the turf had been treated with Methoxone (M.C.P.A.) prior to sale, doubts arose regarding the effects of selective weed-killers applied prior to lifting. Applications of 2, 4-D (D.C.P.A.) or M.C.P.A. normally produce a depressed effect upon the grasses. Is this depression shared by the roots as well as the visible leaves? And is root extension retarded? Treating secures weed elimination or reduction and enables better turf to be offered, but it would be advisable when purchasing treated turf to inquire when treatment was made for it would appear that lifting and laying should be deferred when selective weed-killers are applied.

LAYING

The most opportune times for laying are during late autumn or early winter, but in practice the work continues until well into the spring. When turfing, the unturfed ground should be faced standing on a board to prevent foot indentations in the turf already laid. It is advisable to begin in a corner or on one side and work across the site, laying the turves with the crevices alternating. When laying is completed, a dressing of sand should be given and worked well into the joints with a straight-edge. Rolling with a 2 cwt. roller is advised, moving the roller in the direction the turves were laid. Rolling may have to be repeated if frost causes the turves to lift.

Turf laid during the autumn or early winter will benefit by composting in the early spring, applying at the rate of 1 lb. per square yard. Rosette weeds should be removed with a hand fork as they appear, but selective weed-killers should not be applied until the sward is well rooted and established.

PATCHING

Weak or thin turf is normally renovated by sowing lawn grass seeds, but areas receiving excessive wear such as the base lines of lawn tennis courts, are usually returfed annually. The worn turves are lifted, the soil forked, consolidated by rolling or treading, and dressed with bone meal at the rate of 2 oz. per square yard. A spade or turfing iron is inserted under the surrounding turf to the extent of about 2 ft. and sifted soil packed underneath so that the final level is about ¾ in. higher than originally. The new turves are laid, dressed with sand, and rolled.

TURF NURSERIES

For the renovation of sports turf it is highly desirable to cultivate a reserve or turf nursery with the object of having available suitable turves for the particular purpose required. When laying a Cumberland turf bowling green an adequate surplus should be laid and cultivated for repairs at a later date. It is emphasized, however, that unless the nursery is well cultivated, mown, rolled, de-wormed, fed, forked and raked in the same way as the green, court or wicket, then little benefit can follow the laying of this reserve.

A turf nursery is often established but sadly neglected with a result that the sward deteriorates and is not suitable for use when required. It will be appreciated that turf lifted from a bed receiving the same treatment as the lawn or green where it is to be laid, is more likely to prove satisfactory than a sample imported from a distance.

A turf nursery can be sown with lawn grass seeds and cultivation should in no way differ from the normal recommendations for seedling swards.

In view of the difficulty of obtaining supplies of really good turf, production from seeds would bring about a much desired improvement.

Chapter Six

The Herb Lawn

❧❧❧❧ ❦ ❧❧❧❧

Downland turf, soft underfoot, is usually aromatic; the close-textured sward of grasses interspersed with dwarf herbs withstanding close grazing by sheep and rabbits. Those who have walked over the Sussex Downs will know how springy is the turf and how delicious the scent from the footsteps of those walking ahead.

In the valley, also, dwarf herbs and grasses intermingle to form a natural English sward. On the clay soils of Surrey, lying to the south of the North Downs, chamomile will be found in nearly all the village greens.

Uniformity of texture required for many outdoor games has resulted in the indigenous herbs disappearing from lawns and sports greens, in fact many delightful species are regarded as weeds and treated as such.

While the superiority of lawn grasses for field games is undoubted the herb lawn should be cultivated far more than it is to-day. It is true that all dwarf herbs may not wear well but it is possible to form and to maintain a golf green from chamomile as is evidenced by the chamomile greens which at one time were a feature of the course of the Royal Guernsey Golf Club.

The celebrated John Evelyn knew chamomile well, for in his famous *Kalendarium Hortense*, writing under October he states: 'It will now be good to beat, roll and mow carpet walks and chamomile.'

Charm and variety could be added to garden lawns and increased interest brought to ornamental turf in public parks by the establishment of herb lawns.

The time is ripe for a revival of interest in this link with Elizabethan gardens and the following species of dwarf herbs are worthy of a trial.

CHAMOMILE (*Anthemis nobilis*)

A procumbent, much-branched perennial with bipinnate leaves, the segments of which are fine and pointed. The flower heads are solitary

56

on terminal peduncles. This is an indigenous species in southern England and Ireland.

CULTIVATION. The soil for a herb lawn should be prepared by digging one spit deep and pre-treating as recommended prior to laying turves. Plants may be set nine inches apart in rows one foot asunder. It will be appreciated that by planting more closely a carpet-like sward will be produced in a relatively shorter time. An opportune time for planting is during April, but as an alternative to purchasing plants, seeds may be sown during the same month and if the young plants are set in nursery beds they can be grown on for planting during the spring of the following year. Mowing with a scythe or a well-sharpened hand-machine will conduce to the development of a dwarf sward.

Fertilizer treatment will depend upon the condition of the herb lawn and top-dressing annually with compost and general fertilizer at the rate of a pound to the square yard may prove beneficial.

WILD THYME (*Thymus serpyllum*)

A perennial with much-branched, almost woody stems, these being small and fringed. Flowers purple, borne on numerous heads. Very aromatic especially when the weather is hot. To obtain variation of flower colour, *Thymus serpyllum coccineus* and *T. serp. albus* are suggested.

CULTIVATION. Seeds should be sown in shallow drills in April, thinning the seedlings to four inches apart in May or June. Plants purchased or raised from seeds sown the previous year may be planted on the prepared site as advised for chamomile. Vegetative propagation by division is also recommended when stocks exist. In nature this species is found on dry heathland and therefore is capable of withstanding drought. Cutting with a scythe is advised.

Several other species of thyme could be tried, including the following:

Carraway-scented Thyme (*Thymus Herba-barona*)
Lemon Thyme (*Thymus citriodorus*)
Russian Thyme (*Thymus odoratissimus*)

PENNYROYAL (*Mentha Pulegium*)

Egg-shaped, nearly smooth leaves are borne upon prostrate stems with the flowers in distant whorls, purple in colour. Growing wild it is found in wet, heathy places and the whole plant has a most agreeable perfume.

CULTIVATION. This plant is more likely to succeed upon a moist loamy soil and will thrive in partial shade given adequate moisture. Seeds may be sown in spring and summer, or plants set on a prepared site in September, March or April. Stock can be increased by offshoots or divisions in October or March.

Copious supplies of water are required during dry weather and top-dressing annually is recommended. Species worthy of a trial in milder parts of the country are:

Corsican Mint (*Mentha Requienii*)
Gibraltar Mint (*Mentha Pulegium gibraltarica*)

YARROW (*Achillea Millefolium*)

Leaves twice pinnatifid, woolly to slightly hairy with the leaflets cut into hair-like segments. Flowers borne in dense terminal corymbs. A common plant by roadsides, and it has a strong aromatic odour.

CULTIVATION. Regarded as a weed of sports turf, this species has immense powers of drought resistance and is capable of establishing itself upon a variety of soils. Seeds may be sown broadcast over the prepared site at the rate of half an ounce to the square yard and lightly raked in. The young plants should be thinned where necessary, using the thinnings to fill gaps.

Top dressing is not normally required and the minimum of moisture is necessary to support a sward.

Chapter Seven

Maintaining a Garden Lawn

⋙ ∘ ⋘

There are many good garden lawns, but far too many mediocre and bad ones, in fact, the standard of lawn turf cultivation in town and country gardens compares unfavourably with that of the sports ground and golf course. Lawns are often sown or laid with great care and attention to detail, yet frequently an inferior seeds mixture or poor turves are used, with the result that the gardener commences with a handicap and in despair decides that the velvet, close-textured sward is not for him.

Garden lovers who produce flowers and vegetables of the highest quality often fail to grow and maintain a lawn which should be the central feature of the garden scheme. Soil pre-treatment with fertilizers, the destruction of weeds prior to sowing, the choice of a suitable seeds mixture or the selection of good turves, and correct maintenance in the early stages, all play their parts.

Planning is necessary, yet so seldom attempted; the lawn, like Topsy, is expected to 'just grow'. Growth, however, is not enough, the sward must be weed free, dense, and of good colour. Grasses produce basal buds from which, under suitable conditions, side-shoots known as 'tillers' will develop and the power of a sward to tiller is not only dependent upon the species of grasses forming the turf but is influenced by mowing, raking, and top dressing. The prevention and control of insect pests and fungoid diseases is also important and suitable measures must be taken.

Top dressing, perhaps the key to better lawns, is seldom regular; so often the turf is allowed to deteriorate and then compost is applied, yet regular dressings should be given commencing with the establishment of the seedling sward. A dressing of:

> 2 parts sifted soil
> 2 parts peat (granulated)
> 1 part sand (sharp)

will be found satisfactory upon the majority of soils but it is important that it be finely screened to avoid damage to the mower. The quantity to be used may vary from one to two pounds per square yard but it is unwise to economize, for to spare the compost is to spoil the sward. Compost dressings should be worked into the turf with the back of the rake.

Planned cultivation is essential to maintain the finest-quality sward, for mowing and rolling for a hundred years will not bring success if unaccompanied by feeding, spiking, watering, and raking at the proper times.

The Lawn in Springtime

When the garden wakes from the winter, spring—gay with the early flowers—should herald a period of activity for the lawn owner. Mowing is usually postponed until too late in the season but it should be borne in mind that if the soil is not too soft for the mower or the grasses affected by the frost, mowing can take place at any time of the year.

In normal seasons mowing can commence at the end of February or early in March, with the machine set high, and the cut should be gradually taken lower until the grasses are mown to the desired length in April. The height to which the turf is mown is a subject of some controversy but unless the sward is required for bowls or putting it is unnecessary to cut lower than a quarter of an inch. Experiments prove that turf mown keenly is more susceptible to moss invasion for moss needs light to develop and a close-cropped turf provides a more congenial home for this invader.

After the winter rains have washed many plant foods from the soil the return to more rapid leaf growth calls for feeding, and fertilizer application with complementary top dressing is advised. A suggested manurial programme is outlined in Chapter Thirteen.

Where weeds are troublesome, treatment with selective weed-killers is suggested but when the re-establishment of the sward by sowing seeds is planned, then a selective weed-killer containing the ethyl ester or amine salt of 2, 4-D is recommended. 'Dicotox' and 'Weed-kill' are reliable proprietary brands obtainable from seedsmen, chemists, and horticultural sundriesmen. Sowing can take place at once without fear of a marked reduction in germination when this type of selective weed-killer is applied. If, however, a formula containing Methoxone is used it is wise to defer sowing for three months.

Where worms are excessively troublesome, the application of mowrah meal or one of the many excellent proprietary worm-killers will be necessary but lawn owners should not destroy worms merely in imitation of the professional greenkeeper or groundsman who, upon the tennis court and putting and bowling green is required to produce a surface which is true and not slippery. Worm casts can be swept into the sward and unless there is a high worm population rendering the surface unfavourable for the growth of the grasses, worm destruction is not essential. Rolling wet turf induces consolidation and lack of aeration. While it is necessary for cricket wickets and tennis courts to produce a true surface, the garden lawn need not be true nor, in fact, level. Providing the undulation of the surface does not interfere with mowing, there is no reason to endeavour slavishly to produce a sports green finish, yet so many gardeners roll whenever the turf is moist. Rolling dry turf produces a beneficial wave-like movement and provides aeration, and lawn turf should be rolled when dry. Where it is necessary to correct serious differences in levels this can be effected by lifting, followed by relaying or sowing or by top-dressing.

The Lawn in Summer

Mowing three or four times a week is the ideal and except where *Poa annua* or Yorkshire fog are troublesome, the grass-box can be removed from the mower during the hot days of summer; for the mowings will act as a mulch, conserving moisture. Raking is too seldom a routine operation, being relegated to spring and autumn for the collection of fallen leaves, but the use of a wire rake of the 'Springbok' type during the summer months will not only prevent the formation of matted growth but will encourage the basal buds to break and so cover the surface.

Pricking with a solid-tined fork during a period of dry weather will open the soil, and water will be absorbed more readily. The application and absorption of water are of great importance in turf maintenance and many failures are due to a deterioration of the grasses through a lack of surface moisture. When the soil is dry, weeds and weed-grasses usurp the more desirable species. A good lawn turf cannot be maintained without the guarantee of an adequate water supply. Sprinklers of many types are available and contrary to popular belief, little damage is likely to follow their use in bright sunshine. They can be used day or night, providing air or soil temperatures are not low, for greater damage is likely to be suffered by turf which is excessively dry than that watered at what is considered to be an inopportune time.

Where weed destruction is planned using a selective weed-killer of the Methoxone group, treatment should take place not later than the month of May if renovation by sowing lawn grass seeds during the late summer or early autumn is contemplated.

Dressing with fertilizers and the application of compost should form part of the summer programme.

The Lawn in Autumn

During the early autumn days fungal diseases are likely to make an appearance, although where turf is watered regularly these might well occur at any time of the year. The use of quick-acting nitrogenous fertilizers is not advised at this period, for they are likely to produce a lax type of growth susceptible to fungal organisms. Forking with a hollow-pronged fork during the autumn months will be found very beneficial, for these forks provide aeration, correct over-consolidation, and prune the roots of the grasses. The use of a fork of this type is recommended before composting, for the compost can then be worked into the holes. Seeding or the laying of turves, and attention to their subsequent requirements, should normally complete the programme.

Chapter Eight

Worms

❯❯❯❯❯ ◦ ❮❮❮❮❮

The old maxim that 'a worm in a garden is worth a farthing' does not hold good when applied to the production of sports turf, where an excess of worms becomes a serious menace, and if remedial measures are not taken the sward deteriorates rapidly. Slimy casts cover the surface and when rolled or trodden upon are flattened out, smothering many of the finer grasses. Worm casts often contain a large proportion of undesirable subsoil and appear to be seed beds for weeds and weed-grasses.

Zoologists tell us that worms originally inhabited the sea, which would account for their preference for low-lying, wet and badly drained soils.

When Beale[1] first advocated worm killing upon golf greens the proposal met with considerable opposition from people who considered it contrary to nature, the strongest argument being that worms assisted in the aeration of the soil and the drainage of the turf, by forming a multitude of small tunnels. This advantage, however, is considerably outweighed by the many disadvantages of a worm-infested sward and as aeration can be effected by forking and spiking, the worm (at least in sports turf) must go, or the finest and truest sward cannot be maintained.

Worms are usually nearer the surface during warm, moist weather, but are found at depths up to six feet when the weather is dry, hot or cold. During breeding seasons, normally from the end of March until May, and from the end of August until November, they work near to the surface and at these times their destruction is more readily brought about.

In addition to the worm-killers described there are many excellent proprietary brands offered which are very effective; the directions given are clear and concise and the materials are easy to handle. The most

[1] Beale, R.: *Lawns for Sports.*

popular also have the great advantage of being non-poisonous. The following are well-known worm-killers:

MOWRAH MEAL (Non-poisonous)

The seeds of an East Indian and Malayan tree (*Bassia latifolia*) are used for the extraction of an oil used for soap making; the residue is mowrah meal, a most popular and successful worm-killer.

It is, however, of little use unless ground to a very fine powder, and it must at all times be kept dry before applying. Leave the turf unrolled for several days to allow the worms to open up their runs. Then a dull, misty, warm day should be chosen for the application and it is advisable to treat two or three square yards before attempting to 'deworm' a large area, for if the worms do not rise freely it is advisable to postpone treatment until conditions are favourable.

Apply at the rate of six to eight ounces per square yard and thoroughly water in, using as much water as possible—the greater the force the better the result. For this reason a pressure spray is recommended. Some groundsmen prefer to mix the meal in a tank and then to pump it on to the turf, but generally speaking it is considered best to spread the meal and then to water it in.

BLUESTONE OR COPPER SULPHATE (Poisonous)

As in the case of mowrah meal, copper sulphate acts as an irritant to the worms, but whereas the former, containing 2 to 3 per cent of nitrogen in organic form, has manurial properties, copper sulphate plays only an indirect part in turf maintenance. It brings about worm destruction, but contains no nutrient material.

When preparing copper sulphate for use, suspend a bag containing the crystals from the rim of a wooden barrel containing water. It is most important that wooden vessels be used, as copper sets up chemical action and corrosion when remaining in contact with metal.

The proportion for use is $\frac{1}{2}$ lb. copper sulphate to 25 gallons of water, which makes a solution to treat 50 square yards. Pump the solution on to the turf, or water by means of a can, and be sure to wash the can after use to remove traces of copper.

The material has proved itself quick-acting, but an obvious disadvantage is the fact that it is a corrosive poison. In its favour, it can be said that it appears to succeed when atmospheric conditions can be considered unsuitable for applying mowrah meal, and also it is a very valuable fungicide.

LEAD ARSENATE (Poisonous)

Where water cannot be obtained lead arsenate is a valuable worm-killer. The usual rate of application is two ounces per square yard, mixed with an equal quantity of finely sifted soil on light soils, or fine coke breeze, in the same proportion, upon heavy land.

Lead arsenate is comparatively slow to act, and might take as long as six months, although results can sometimes be observed in a fortnight.

PERCHLORIDE OF MERCURY OR CORROSIVE SUB-LIMATE (Poisonous)

After weighing carefully its value as a worm-killer with a danger which exists in handling such a highly poisonous material, it is not recommended that this be used by amateur gardeners. Skilled greenkeepers should be very well trained before attempting to apply.

To avoid handling, perchloride of mercury can be purchased in three-ounce packets, sufficient to dissolve in fifty gallons of water, and to treat one thousand square feet. There is, however, a danger of scorching, and the application of an additional fifty gallons of water to the same area is recommended. Wooden vessels must be used, as corrosive sublimate attacks metal.

PERMANGANATE OF POTASH (Non-poisonous)

This has, on many sports grounds, proved an effective worm-killer with the advantage of being cheap and comparatively easy to apply. For worm destruction on garden lawns it has a great deal to recommend it, both in simplicity and effectiveness.

The solution is made by dissolving $\frac{1}{2}$ oz. permanganate of potash in 1 gallon of water, and this is sufficient to treat 1 square yard. When mixing, add the crystals to the water, and leave for ten minutes to dissolve.

DERRIS (Non-poisonous)

Derris powder has a world-wide reputation as an insecticide, being known as a contact and stomach poison to most invertebrates. While derris is regarded as non-poisonous to most animals, it is a fish poison, and should not be used where it is likely to contaminate water containing fish.

Derris powder applied to turf at the rate of $\frac{1}{2}$ to 1 oz. per square yard, and watered in with 1 gallon of water per square yard will be found very

E   65

effective, although normally worms do not rise immediately after the application. It will, however, be noted that large numbers comparable with those brought up by the use of mowrah meal will appear the next day and, furthermore, the majority of the worms will be dead.

It appears to be superior in the duration of its effectiveness, and it has been suggested that it is capable of destroying the eggs of the earthworm. The natural suggestion is a combination of mowrah meal and derris; and in recent experiments it has been found that application of a mixture of 4 oz. of mowrah meal and 1 oz. of derris per square yard, has not only raised worms immediately under favourable conditions, but the worm population has remained low over a longer period.

Chapter Nine

Weeds

᠈᠈᠈᠈ ∘ ᠄᠄᠄᠄

We must be prepared for a reversal of values when comparing the plants which compose a good sward suitable for golf greens, tennis courts, bowling greens, and cricket pitches, with those found in leys and permanent pasture on the farm.

Farmers esteem wild white clover very highly as a component of a mixture of grasses and clovers for land to be laid down to grass, but its appearance on a bowling green is likely to cause consternation. Similarly, rib-grass—loathed by cricketers—is often included in agricultural grass-land as it has a high nutritive value and is relished by sheep. Fescues and bents, components of the finest sea-washed turf, if found in a high pro-portion in pasture are regarded with little favour by the farmer.

Weeds in lawns and sports turf cannot be tolerated, for they not only detract from the appearance of the sward, but when ball games are played upon them, results are erratic. Gardeners know that plants are divided into three classes according to their longevity:

1. ANNUALS

Weeds which appear, flower, produce seeds and die, thus complet-ing their life cycle, within one year, are known as annuals. Generally speaking, they are not very troublesome in turf, as close mowing pre-vents them from seeding. They are, however, likely to occur in newly sown lawns and greens, and as described earlier, they must be removed in the early stages before they set their seeds. There are two which must be mentioned, parsley piert and annual meadow-grass, for although closely mown, they can still produce seeds, and the annual meadow-grass in particular can prove a serious menace.

2. BIENNIALS

These require two years to complete their life cycle. During the firs-year, vegetative growth takes place but flowers and seeds are not prot

duced until the second year. After setting the seeds they die. There are few biennial weeds found in turf, wild carrot and spear thistle are, however, discovered at various times.

3. PERENNIALS

These have no definite time of existence, for by underground or overground runners or stolons they can continue to increase. Most of the common turf weeds are found in this class, examples being dandelions, daisies and buttercups.

THE HARMFUL EFFECTS OF WEEDS

Weeds cause overcrowding, the grasses competing with the aggressive weeds and being robbed of food and water. A turf with a heavy weed infestation is thus certain to deteriorate rapidly. During periods of dry weather the onset of drought conditions is hastened by the moisture transpired by the broader-leaved weeds, which also act as host plants for fungoid diseases and provide shelter for insect pests.

The most troublesome weeds are those which by their habit of growth can escape the mower blades or in spite of cutting produce flowers and seeds at a very low level, thus increasing their numbers in the sward.

DISTRIBUTION

Weeds can be propagated in the same way as any cultivated plant, i.e. by seeds, cuttings, or runners. The seeds or fruits of many are so designed to ensure their wide dispersal—the dandelion is an example. Birds in their droppings also aid dispersal.

Couch grass and sheep sorrel are examples of weeds with rhizomes which not only colonize the turf around them but spread to new areas. The bulbous buttercup propagates itself by small offsets from the parent bulb.

Care must be taken when applying soil in the form of compost, for weeds can be introduced in large numbers if the ingredients are not sterilized. Care in the choice of fertilizers is essential. Phosphatic and potassic manures when applied alone without nitrogen have a tendency to promote the growth of clovers. A discussion on the relative merits of lime will be found in a later chapter and it would appear from the evidence we have before us that lime tends to make weeds flourish; but here again the problem cannot be dismissed lightly by saying the lime is not required to maintain any or every type of soil-carrying lawn turf.

Lawns and Playing-Field Weeds

(a) CLOVERS (Natural Order: *Leguminosæ*)

Here we meet a group of plants greatly esteemed by farmers and strangely enough tolerated by many when found in ornamental lawns. On cricket pitches, tennis courts, bowling and golf greens they are, however, intolerable and must be removed. They are slippery and dangerous when the faster-moving games are played and prevent the ball moving in an even manner to make the full enjoyment of bowls, golf and cricket possible. They should be excluded from any prescriptions of grasses for fine lawns and sports grounds.

Clovers belong to the same family as peas, french beans, broad beans, runner beans and sweet peas and the flower consists of five petals, the larger, and most conspicuous, being known as the 'standard', the laterals termed 'wings' and the two anterior petals the 'keel'. In common with the other members of this family they can absorb and fix the free nitrogen of the air by means of nodule bacteria upon their roots. This is, however, no recommendation for their presence in fine turf as nitrogen can be applied in the form of fertilizers without having to tolerate clovers.

YELLOW SUCKLING CLOVER   HOP CLOVER

YELLOW SUCKLING CLOVER (*Trifolium minus.* Sm: *Trifolium dubium* Sibth). (Annuals)

BOTANICAL DESCRIPTION. A slender annual much branched at the base, glabrous or slightly downy, procumbent. Stipules broad and pointed. Leaflets obovate or obcordate, the central one at some distance from the others. Flower heads loosely globular or ovoid, containing 12–20 small pale yellow flowers on very short pedicles; in fading the flowers become reflexed and turn pale brown, concealing the one-seeded pod.

NOTES. This plant is sometimes confused with black medick (*Medicago lupulina*, Linn.) because the leaflets of both are trifoliate and the flower head very similar. They can, however, be distinguished as in black medick the mid-rib is extended to a short point at the end of the leaflet, whereas it is not in yellow suckling clover.

HOP CLOVER (*Trifolium procumbens*, Linn.; *Trifolium campestre*, Schreb.) (Annual)

BOTANICAL DESCRIPTION. A glabrous or slightly downy annual, branches at the base; procumbent or nearly erect, 6 in. to 1 ft. long. Stipules broad and pointed. Leaflets obovate or obcordate, the central one at some distance from the remainder. Flower heads loosely globular, or ovoid, on rather long axillary peduncles, containing from 30 to 50 small yellow flowers on very long pedicles: when the flower fades it becomes reflexed and turns pale brown, with a broadly obovate standard concealing the small, one-seeded pod.

NOTES. A very common British plant, which is found chiefly on dry soils.

BIRD'S-FOOT TREFOIL

BIRD'S-FOOT TREFOIL (*Lotus corniculatus*, Linn.). (Perennial)

BOTANICAL DESCRIPTION. Stock perennial with a long taproot. Stems decumbent or ascending from a few inches to near 2 feet long.

Leaflets usually much longer than the leaves. Umbels of from 5 or 6 to twice that number of bright yellow flowers: the standard often red on the outside. Pod usually about an inch long. Seeds globular, separated by a pithy substance which nearly fills the pod.

BLACK MEDICK OR NONSUCH (*Medicago lupulina*, Linn.). (Annual)

BOTANICAL DESCRIPTION. A spreading branching annual with stems up to 2 ft. long, covered with short soft hairs. Stipules broad and shortly toothed. Leaflets obovate with midribs extending to a short point. Peduncles longer than the leaves, bearing an oblong head of very small bright yellow flowers.

Pods small with one seed which is black when ripe, glabrous or slightly hairy. Kidney shaped and marked with veins and curved spirally.

NOTES. Often confused with yellow Suckling clover (*Trifolium minus*) but can be distinguished by the short pointed extension of the midrib on each leaflet.

BLACK MEDICK OR NONSUCH   WHITE OR DUTCH CLOVER

WHITE OR DUTCH CLOVER (*Trifolium repens*, Linn.). (Perennial)

BOTANICAL DESCRIPTION. A glabrous or slightly hairy perennial, the stems creeping and rooting at the nodes. Leaflets obovate, distinctly toothed and bearing a mark in the centre which resembles a horseshoe. The leaf stalks are often very long.

71

Peduncles axillary, long and erect, bearing a globular umbel of white flowers, often tinged with pink. Pod containing 2–4 seeds usually protruding from the calyx, but enclosed in the withered corolla.

Notes. During dry seasons the stems often fail to root at the nodes, and assume an arched position contributing to an uneven surface. The taproot is strong and well developed, often descending to a depth of 8–12 inches.

RED OR PURPLE CLOVER (*Trifolium pratense*, Linn.). (Perennial)

Botanical Description. Stock usually perennial but of few years' duration. Stems decumbent or near erect, 1–2 feet long and hairy. Stipules rather larger, ovate, veined with large green points. Leaflets obovate or obcordate. Flowers reddish-purple in dense terminal, ovoid or globular heads with two sessile, trifoliate leaves close at their base. Calyx—teeth subulate and hairy, the lowest longer than the others. After flowering, the petals turn brown, the calyx remains erect, enclosing usually a simple seed pod.

Notes. This is a taller-growing plant normally absent from closely mown turf but sometimes found in golf fairways and sports fields.

Eradication. Clovers cannot withstand constant close mowing or scything. Owing to their low creeping habit they are likely to be missed by the mower, but raking up prior to mowing or scything is advised. Dusting in early March with

> 1 part sulphate of iron
> 1 part sulphate of ammonia
> 2 parts dried blood
> 4 parts dry sand

has been found effective and persistent applications of lawn sand are also useful. Spraying with proprietary selective weed-killers reduces clovers but does not eliminate them. Phosphatic and potassic manures have a tendency to encourage their establishment.

(b) THE COMPOSITE FAMILY (NATURAL ORDER *Compositæ*)

This is the most extensive family among flowering plants and represented in every quarter of the globe. It is also most easily recognized as the flowers, which have the appearance of being single, are actually clusters of flowers collected together in a head, the whole having the appearance of one blossom. These florets are of two types, the disc floret being short and tubular while the ray florets have a long ligulate petal and are arranged round the disc. In some genera however, the flower heads consist wholly of disc florets or in others ray florets.

DAISY (*Bellis perennis*, Linn.). (Perennial)

BOTANICAL DESCRIPTION. Stock perennial, tufted. Leaves radical, obovate, or oblong slightly toothed. Peduncles also radical, obovate or oblong, bearing single flower heads. Involucre green, nearly glabrous.

DAISY

YARROW OR MILFOIL

Florets of the ray ligulate, white or tinged with pink. Those of the disc numerous, small and tubular.

NOTES. Probably the most common weed found in turf. It flowers for most of the year, and the leaves are pressed so close to the soil as to smother the finer grasses. This habit allows the plant to escape being cut by a mowing-machine.

When cutting lawns infested with daisies, the box should always be in position, otherwise seeds may be spread to the surrounding turf.

ERADICATION. Lawn sand destroys daisies readily, and should be used in accordance with the directions of the manufacturer. They are, however, resistant to selective weed-killers and several applications may be necessary.

YARROW OR MILFOIL (*Achillea Millefolium*, Linn.). (Perennial)

BOTANICAL DESCRIPTION. Stock perennial, creeping underground, with numerous short leafy branches, and almost simple erect flowering stems. Leaves oblong or linear in their outline, but finally cut into numerous short but very narrow and deeply pinnatifid segments, from which the plant derives its botanical name 'mellefolium' (thousand-leaved). The leaves are woolly or nearly hairless. Flowers aggregated together white or occasionally purplish, common on all pastures.

NOTES. This weed spreads rapidly by means of runners above and below the ground. Its inclusion in prescriptions for aerodromes is common and it is also used for grazing. When trodden upon and bruised it gives off a characteristic odour.

ERADICATION. Raking up and mowing closely, weakens the plant and lawn sand applied persistently is sometimes successful but there is a danger that such large quantities may be required as ultimately to impair the health of the lawn grasses. Resistant to selective weed-killers.

In seedling turf a very sharp look-out should be maintained and young plants removed at an early stage. The weed must never gain the ascendancy.

In preference to destroying by chemical treatment the removal of colonies and re-turfing is advised.

CAT'S-EAR

DANDELION

CAT'S-EAR (*Hypochœris radicata*, Linn.). (Perennial)

BOTANICAL DESCRIPTION. Rootstock perennial. Leaves all radical, spreading narrow, more or less toothed or pinnately lobed, hispid on both sides with stiff hairs. Stalks erect and leafless, one to two feet high and usually divided into two or three long branches, terminating into a rather large-headed flower. Flowers yellow, fruit bearing a feathery parachute carried by wind.

NOTES. This is a very common lawn and sports ground weed found in all soils; but more frequent on light land. It is very drought-resistant and thrives even when closely mown, reproducing from the strong, thick tap-root.

ERADICATION. Small numbers can be removed with a weed fork, but when turf is heavily invaded treatment with selective weed-killers will be found effective.

DANDELION (*Taraxacum dens-leonis*, Desf. *Taraxacum officinale*, Web.). (Perennial)

BOTANICAL DESCRIPTION. The root stock, black on the outside and very bitter, descends into a thick tap-root. Leaves variable from linear to lanceolate and almost entire to deeply pinnatifid, with broad triangular lobes, pointing downwards in most plants, the terminal one larger, obovate or acute.

Peduncles 2–6 or sometimes 8 inches high. Involucral bracts linear often thickened towards the top. Achenes slightly compressed, striated, marked upwards with short pointed asperites, the beak two or three times as long as the achene itself.

NOTES. In dry seasons dandelions appear most troublesome, but this is most likely due to their being able to stand adverse conditions, far better than the surrounding grasses, which are weak and thin. It is essential that they should be prevented from flowering and setting seeds.

ERADICATION. The weed is very susceptible to applications of selective weed-killers.

COLTSFOOT (*Tussilago Farfara*, Linn.). (Perennial)

BOTANICAL DESCRIPTION. Rootstock perennial, creeping. Leaves radical, deeply cordate. Flowering stems simple but often growing in tufts, erect, about six inches high, more or less covered with loose white cotton. Flower heads solitary terminal bright yellow.

Radical leaves appearing much later than the flower stems, four or five inches broad, angular and toothed, covered underneath with loose white cottony-wool of which there is a little also upon the upper side.

NOTES. Not a very troublesome weed but one which is often found in fields taken over for building purposes or converted into sports grounds and when the land is reseeded for garden lawns, golf courses, or for cricket or tennis, it may prove a nuisance.

The flowers which are sometimes confused with the dandelion appear in February and March and set seeds before the leaves, which resemble in outline the imprint of a colt's foot, make their appearance. Thorough fallowing prior to sowing seeds is therefore essential.

ERADICATION. Repeated defoliation by mowing, rapidly exhausts the plant. Fallowing and removing roots before sowing will limit the chance of an infestation. Susceptible to selective weed-killers.

LESSER HAWKBIT (*Leontodon hirtus*, Linn.). (Perennial)

BOTANICAL DESCRIPTION. A glabrous perennial, sometimes with a few stiff, mostly forked hairs on the leaves and lower parts of the peduncles.

LESSER HAWKBIT

Leaves oblong or linear coarsely toothed sinuate or shortly pinnatifid.

Peduncles seldom above six inches high, with a single, rather small head of bright yellow flowers.

76

Involucres green and glabrous consisting of ten or twelve nearly equal bracts.

Achenes slightly tapering at the top with a short, scaly pappus.

NOTES. Fairly common in England and Ireland, but found only in the south-east of Scotland.

ERADICATION. Spraying or dusting with selective weed-killers very effective.

THISTLES

As a general rule not very troublesome but appear in newly sown swards. Mowing regularly precludes their establishment and in most cases they disappear within two or three years from sowing.

CREEPING THISTLE

SPEAR THISTLE

CREEPING THISTLE (*Carduus arvensis*, Curt. *Cirsium arvense*, Scop.). (Perennial)

BOTANICAL DESCRIPTION. Rootstock perennial and creeping, with erect annual stems three to four feet high. Leaves narrow and pinnatifid, very prickly, either embracing the stem with prickly auricles or shortly decurrant.

Flower heads not large, forming rather loose terminal corymbs, and always dioecious, the males nearly globular with very projecting purple florets, the females with much longer involucres but shorter florets.

NOTES. This weed is a source of concern to the farmer, but its inability to withstand close mowing reduces its danger as a lawn weed to a minimum. It increases chiefly by means of its root system and when stems and leaves are killed by frost the root system survives. An aid to identification is that the purplish flowers have an odour very strongly resembling that of honey.

ERADICATION. Close mowing is essential. Removing with a weed-fork or injecting weed-killer into the crowns is also recommended. Thorough preparation before sowing will prevent infestation. Reduced by selective weed-killers, but two or more applications may be required to destroy survivors.

SPEAR THISTLE (*Carduus lanceolatus*, Linn. *Cirsium lanceolatum*, Scop.). (Biennial)

BOTANICAL DESCRIPTION. Under the International Rules of Botanical nomenclature this species is now known as *Cirsium vulgare*, Airg-Shaw.

NOTES. When found in closely mown turf the foliage is usually a rosette and the plant does not flower under these conditions.

ERADICATION. Same as for creeping thistle.

MARSH THISTLE

DWARF THISTLE

MARSH THISTLE (*Carduus palustris*, Linn.). (Annual or Biennial)

BOTANICAL DESCRIPTION. A stiff annual or biennial, 4–5 feet high. Leaves narrow, the lower ones 6–8 inches long, pinnatifid with numerous ovate, wavy, prickly lobes with a few rough hairs scattered on both surfaces, the upper leaves small and very narrow. Flower heads rather numerous, small, ovoid, usually collected in clusters, forming an irregular terminal corymb. Involucre bracts numerous, with small somewhat prickly points, the inner ones often coloured. Florets purple.

NOTES. Forms a rosette in closely mown lawns and persists for several years.

ERADICATION. Same as for creeping thistle.

DWARF THISTLE (*Cirsium acaule*, Weber). (Perennial)

BOTANICAL DESCRIPTION. When growing in pasture it is distinguished by the almost complete lack of stem.

It is perennial, woody, thick and bears a spreading tuft of very prickly pinnatifid and glabrous leaves, in the midst of which are a few rather large sessile flower heads.

Involucres ovoid, not cottony, with numerous lanceolate, obtuse or scarcely pointed bracts. Florets purple.

NOTES. Mostly found in turf overlaying chalk, the rosette habit smothering the fine grasses.

ERADICATION. Same as for creeping thistle.

SOW THISTLE (*Sonchus oleraceus*, Linn.). (Annual)

BOTANICAL DESCRIPTION. Stem thick and hollow, 1–3 or even 4 feet high, glabrous with occasionally a few stiff hairs on the peduncles.

Leaves thin, pinnatifid with broad, heart-shaped or triangular terminal lobes, bordered with irregular, pointed or prickly teeth and a few smaller lobes or coarse teeth along the broad leaf-stalk.

Flower heads rather small in a short corymbose panicle sometimes almost umbellate.

Achenes flattened, with longitudinal ribs, the pappus numerous snow-white hairs.

NOTES. Although a tall-growing weed it is able to adopt a 'rosette' habit and survive in closely mown turf. Seeds are spread by the parachute attached to them.

ERADICATION. Same as for creeping thistle.

RAGWORT (*Senecio Jacobea*, Linn.). (Biennial or Perennial)

BOTANICAL DESCRIPTION. Rootstock, short and thick, without creeping shoots. Stems 2–4 feet high, erect, scarcely branches except at the tops. Leaves pinnate, with ovate, obovate or narrow segments, coarsely toothed or pinnatifid; the terminal one large and confluent, the lower ones smaller and distinct, all glabrous or with a loose, woolly down, especially on the underside. Flower heads rather large of a bright yellow in a handsome compact terminal corymb. Involucral bracts tipped with black, the outer ones few and very small. Florets of the ray from 12 to 15, linear oblong and spreading. Achenes of the disc covered with short hairs, those of the ray glabrous.

NOTES. In turf which is mown regularly the plant assumes a spreading or small rosette habit and may be mistaken for the water senecio (*Senecio aquaticus*, Hads.). It can be distinguished by examining the achenes or fruits which enclose the seeds. In the ragwort those of the disc or centre are covered with short hairs and only those of the ray are smooth. In the water senecio all are smooth.

The ragwort is not a serious weed in lawns or greens. It may occur in the 'rough' on golf courses.

ERADICATION. Hand-forking and close mowing are sufficient in most cases.

RAGWORT   GROUNDSEL

GROUNDSEL (*Senecio vulgaris*, Linn.). (Annual)

BOTANICAL DESCRIPTION. An erect branching annual from six inches to nearly a foot high, glabrous or bearing a little loose cottony-wool. Leaves pinnatifid, with ovate toothed or jagged lobes. Flower heads in loose terminal corymbs or clusters. Involucres cylindrical of about twenty equal bracts with several smaller ones. Florets almost

5a. Ragwort

5b. Wild Carrot

6. Chamomile

always all tubular, with very, very rarely any ray whatever. Achenes slightly hairy.

NOTES. Very seldom appears in established turf but is common in newly sown lawns.

Thorough cleaning and fallowing as described in earlier chapters should reduce the chances of a serious invasion.

ERADICATION. Hand-weeding is not normally necessary. Cutting newly sown lawns before the weed flowers will destroy.

MOUSE-EAR HAWKWEED   SMOOTH CREPIS OR HAWK'S-BEARD

MOUSE-EAR HAWKWEED (*Hieracium Pilosella*, Linn.). (Perennial)

BOTANICAL DESCRIPTION. Stock perennial, with spreading tufts of radical leaves and creeping leafy shoots. Leaves oblong or lanceolate, entire, tapering at the base and often stalked, green above, with a few long hairs, white underneath, with short down. Peduncles radical with a single head of lemon-coloured flowers often tinged with red on the outside. Involucres and upper part of the peduncle often clothed with a minute and close whitish down, mixed with short stiff spreading black hairs. Achenes shorter in proportion to the pappus than in other species.

NOTES. A very common British weed, but seldom seen upon lawns. Found in the 'rough' and on fairways of golf courses, particularly on acid heaths. The plant forms a dense mat, creeping like a strawberry.

ERADICATION. Very susceptible to spraying or dusting with selective weed-killers but where colonized extensively, lifting and replacing with clean turf may be necessary.

F   81

SMOOTH CREPIS OR HAWK'S-BEARD (*Crepis virens*, Linn. *Crepis capillaris*). (Annual or Biennial)

BOTANICAL DESCRIPTION. An erect or ascending branched annual or biennial from one foot high. Leaves linear or lanceolate, toothed or pinnatifid with triangular or narrow but short lobes; the radical ones stalked, the upper ones clasping the stem by pointed spreading auricles. Flower heads small in loose, often leafy panicles. Involucres often slightly hispid and become conical after flowering. Achenes narrow, oblong but not beaked.

NOTES. This weed is widely distributed, being found wild on dry banks, roadsides and waste places. During dry seasons it is often very troublesome in lawns and sports grounds.

ERADICATION. Resistant to lawn sand. Treatment with selective weed-killers moderately effective under favourable conditions.

KNAPWEED OR HARD HEADS   OX-EYE DAISY

KNAPWEED OR HARD HEADS (*Centaurea nigra*, Linn.). (Perennial)

BOTANICAL DESCRIPTION. A perennial with erect stems, hard and branched, 1–2 feet high. Leaves from linear to lanceolate or oblong; the upper ones entire or nearly so, clasping the stem at their base, the lower ones with a few coarse teeth or short lobes; all green and rather rough with a few minute hairs or slightly cottony underneath when young. Involucres globular on terminal peduncles, the bracts closely imbricated so as only to show their appendages which are brown or black and deeply fringed except on the innermost bracts, where they are shining and usually jagged.

Florets purple. Achenes slightly hairy.

NOTES. Occurs chiefly on chalky or clay soils. The hairy leaves form patches several square inches in extent in lawns and greens even when closely mown. Common on golf 'fairways'.

ERADICATION. Reduced by selective weed-killers but resistant.

OX-EYE DAISY (*Chrysanthemum Leucanthemum*, Linn.). (Perennial)

BOTANICAL DESCRIPTION. A perennial with erect single or slightly branched stems 1–2 feet high, glabrous or slightly downy. Radical leaves obovate and coarsely toothed in long stalks; stem leaves narrow sessile with a few coarse teeth.

Flower heads solitary on long terminal peduncles and rather large.

Involucre bracts bordered by a brown scarious edge. Florets of the ray white, more than half an inch long, those of the disc, numerous small and yellow.

NOTES. Seldom found in closely mown turf, but occurs in poor grassland and in the 'rough' on golf courses.

ERADICATION. Very susceptible to selective weed-killers.

(c) THE PLANTAIN FAMILY (Natural Order: *Plantaginaceæ*)

This is a small family widely spread over the globe but most abundant in the temperate regions of the old world.

GREATER OR BROAD-LEAVED
PLANTAIN

HOARY PLANTAIN OR
LAMB'S-TONGUE

GREATER OR BROAD-LEAVED PLANTAIN (*Plantago major*, Linn.). (Perennial)

BOTANICAL DESCRIPTION. Rootstock short and thick with fibrous roots. Leaves erect or spreading, broadly ovate often four or five inches long and nearly as broad. Entire or toothed, glabrous or downy with 7 (rarely 9 or sometimes 5) prominent parallel ribs, converging at the base into a rather long footstalk.

Peduncles usually longer than the leaves bearing a long, slender flower spike. Capsule 2 celled with 4–8 seeds in each cell.

NOTES. It is found on most soils but more common on those which are heavy and damp. The leaves die in the autumn and therefore cannot be seen during the winter months. Cutting without the box is likely to scatter the seeds over the turf.

ERADICATION. Susceptible to selective weed-killers.

HOARY PLANTAIN OR LAMB'S-TONGUE (*Plantago media*, Linn.). (Perennial)

BOTANICAL DESCRIPTION. Rootstock, thick, almost woolly, branched and descending to a great depth. Leaves which do not die in the winter are ovate, sessile, and forming a rosette. More or less hoary with a short down. Peduncles long and erect. Spike much shorter and thicker than in *P. major* but longer than *P. lanceolata*. Lilac coloured.

NOTES. Found chiefly in limestone districts. Seldom occurs in Ireland, except where introduced.

ERADICATION. As for greater or broad-leaved plantain.

RIBWORT

RIBWORT (*Plantago lanceolata*, Linn.). (Perennial)

BOTANICAL DESCRIPTION. Rootstock short, thick, woody, branched. Leaves in pasture upstanding but forming a rosette 6 to 8 inches across when closely mown. Each leaf has 3 to 5 veins and more or less tapering into a stalk at the base.

Peduncles longer than the leaves, erect and angular. Spike ovoid or oblong, small. Capsule contains two hemispherical seeds.

NOTES. The long stems are easily cut by the mower but the rosette habit of the foliage will allow the plant to escape. The leaves are evergreen. It grows in all kinds of turf and is widely distributed.

ERADICATION. As for greater or broad-leaved plantain.

BUCKS-HORN PLANTAIN OR STARWEED   SEA PLANTAIN

BUCKS-HORN PLANTAIN OR STARWEED (*Plantago Coronopus*, Linn.). (Annual or Biennial)

BOTANICAL DESCRIPTION. Rootstock short and thick. Leaves forming a rosette one to six inches in diameter, numerous linear or linear-lanceolate, conspicuously lobed, woolly, or almost hairless.

Spikes cylindrical, 1–2 inches long but when growing in turf often only $\frac{1}{4}$ inch long. Ovary has 4 cells each with a single ovule.

Very prevalent in seaside greens and lawns. Introduced inland in sea-washed turf.

NOTES. Very troublesome upon seaside golf and bowling greens and when sea-washed turf is laid for inland lawns, the weed is often brought with it.

ERADICATION. As for greater or broad-leaved plantain.

SEA PLANTAIN (*Plantago maritima*, Linn.) (Perennial)

BOTANICAL DESCRIPTION. Stock very much branched. Leaves narrow linear, fleshy, slightly toothed and woolly at the base. Peduncles cylindrical 1–2 inches long. Flowers smaller than those of *P. lanceolata*. Capsules with two seeds only.

NOTES. The natural habitat of this weed is by the sea, but it can be introduced to inland lawns and greens when sea-washed turf is laid.

ERADICATION. Same as for greater or broad-leaved plantain, care being taken to examine seaside turf before it is laid.

(d) THE PINK FAMILY (Natural Order: *Caryophyllaceæ*)

PEARLWORT (*Sagina procumbens*). (Annual or Perennial)

BOTANICAL DESCRIPTION. A minute annual or perennial 1–2 inches or seldom 3 inches high, sometimes erect from the base, especially at

PEARLWORT	SPURRY, DOTHER OR
	POVERTY WEED

first, but usually branching and decumbent, forming little spreading tufts, usually glabrous, but having often an exceedingly minute glandular down. Leaves small and subulate, joined at the base in a short, broad, scarious sheath, and radical ones longer and often tufted.

Flowers very small, on capillary pedicles, much longer than the leaves.

NOTES. This weed varies a great deal and has been divided into many supposed species known as *S. apetula*, Linn., where the petals are very minute or often absent altogether; and *S. ciliata* Friess; where the branches are more diffuse; and *S. maritima*, Don; a sea-coast variety with firmer and thicker stems and leaves.

When closely mown Pearlwort flowers and sets seeds, and the habit of the plant enables it to escape the mower more successfully than most weeds. It is one of the most common weeds in fine turf and often not objected to owing to its close-growing, even habit.

ERADICATION. Resistant to lawn sand but often responds to systemmatic applications. Scarifying and scything will weaken the plant if the treatment is persistent. Spraying or dusting with selective weed-killers may reduce, but pearlwort is resistant.

SPURRY, DOTHER OR POVERTY WEED (*Spergula arvensis*, Linn.). (Annual)

BOTANICAL DESCRIPTION. A slender annual, branching at the base into several erect or ascending stems six inches to one foot high, glabrous or slightly downy. Leaves almost subulate, one to two inches long, growing six or eight together in opposite clusters, and spreading so as to appear whorled. The scarious stipules sometimes obscure. Flowers small, white on long, slender pedicles, turned down after flowering into terminal forked cymes. Seeds slightly flattened with or without a narrow scarious border.

NOTES. A cornfield weed whose presence is indicative of a lack of lime. Plant has a foetid odour which can be detected at a distance. Common in newly sown turf on acid soils.

ERADICATION. Hand weeding and mowing are usually sufficient.

COMMON CHICKWEED (*Stellaria media*, Cyrill). (Annual)

BOTANICAL DESCRIPTION. A weak, much-branched annual, glabrous with the exception of a line of hairs on one side of the stem and a small number of long ones on the leaf stalk. Leaves small, ovate and pointed, the lower ones stalked and often heart-shaped. The upper sessile and narrower. Flowers small, on rather long pedicles, in irregular forked leafy cymes. Petals shorter than the calyx, deeply cleft with narrow, diverging lobes. Stamens often only five. Styles three.

NOTES. A variety which has been named *S. umbrosa*, Opetz, has acutely tubercled seeds whereas in *S. media* proper these are obtusely tubical. Common chickweed is frequently found in seedling swards.

Thorough preparation of the soil limits the chances of a serious invasion.

ERADICATION. It quickly succumbs to close mowing and being an annual, if prevented from setting seeds it soon dies out.

Selective weed-killers and lawn sand are effective if it makes its appearance in established lawns and greens.

COMMON CHICKWEED

MOUSE-EAR CHICKWEED

MOUSE-EAR CHICKWEED (*Cerastium vulgatum*, Linn.). (Annual)

BOTANICAL DESCRIPTION. A coarsely downy, more or less viscid annual, branching at the base; sometimes dwarf, and much branched at others, loosely ascending to one or even two feet. In turf forms dense matted turves which may survive the winter and suggest the plant is perennial. Radical leaves small, and stalked, stem leaves sessile, from broadly ovate to narrow oblong. Sepals green and downy. Petals seldom exceeding the calyx but often much shorter, sometimes none present. Stamens five or fewer. Capsule when dry cylindrical, often curved and projecting beyond the calyx.

NOTES. A very common weed and one which presents a difficult problem when it establishes itself in lawns and greens. The habit varies. In thin turf it is straggling, but in a dense sward it develops in tufted patches. Sometimes an impurity of lawn grass seeds.

ERADICATION. Susceptible to selective weed-killers.

FIELD CHICKWEED (*Cerastium arvense*, Linn.). (Perennial)

BOTANICAL DESCRIPTION. Stem perennial much branched at the base, the flowering branches ascending to about six inches or more. Leaves crowded in the lower part, narrow lanceolate—linear, more glabrous and less viscid than in *C. vulgatum*. Flowers large and white in loose cymes or rather long pedicles. Sepals three inches long, petals twice that length, cleft near the middle. Capsule oblique usually longer than the calyx.

FIELD CHICKWEED

NOTES. This is often mistaken for Mouse-Ear chickweed (*Cerastium vulgatum*) but can be distinguished as its leaves are narrow, smoother and less viscid. Field chickweed is often found in lawns and greens.

ERADICATION. As for Mouse-Ear chickweed.

(e) THE PURSLANE FAMILY (Natural order: *Portulaceæ*)

BLINKS OR WATER CHICKWEED (*Montia fontana*, Linn.). (Annual)

BOTANICAL DESCRIPTION. A small, glabrous green, somewhat succulent annual, forming dense tufts from 1 to 4 or 5 inches in height, the stems becoming longer and weaker in more watery situations. Leaves opposite, or nearly so, obovate or spatulate. Flowers solitary or in little grouping racemes of two or three, in the axils of the upper leaves. The petals pure white, a little longer than the calyx. Capsules small and globular.

NOTES. Found where there are damp conditions and in nature on the edges of rills where the water is stagnant.

It appears occasionally in closely mown turf and may be introduced when sand from the margins of streams is used for top dressing.

If it becomes established the dense patches are likely to choke the fine grasses.

ERADICATION. Lawn sand and selective weed-killers effective.

BLINKS OR WATER CHICKWEED   PRUNELLA OR SELF HEAL

(f) THE LABIATE FAMILY (Natural order: *Labiatæ*)

PRUNELLA OR SELF HEAL (*Prunella vulgaris*, Linn.). (Perennial)

BOTANICAL DESCRIPTION. Stem procumbent or creeping and rooting at the base with ascending flowering branches usually about two or three inches high. Leaves stalked, ovate and nearly entire. Corolla, violet-purple varying in size and depth of colour, the upper lid over the lower.

NOTES. Sometimes an impurity of lawn grass seeds. Common in lawns and greens, particularly those which have been neglected.

ERADICATION. Lawn sand and selective weed-killers effective.

(g) THE ROSE FAMILY (Natural order: *Rosaceæ*)

This is a large family spread over the globe, but those species which occur in lawns mostly assume a creeping habit.

CINQUEFOIL OR CREEPING CINQUEFOIL (*Potentilla reptans*, Linn.). (Perennial)

BOTANICAL DESCRIPTION. Stock seldom much tufted, with slender

90

prostrate stems often rooting at the nodes, and sometimes extending to a considerable length. Stipules ovate, mostly entire.

Leaves all stalked with five obovate or oblong coarsely toothed leaflets.

Flowers single on long peduncles, axillary. Petals large and yellow. Mostly five but occasionally four.

NOTES. This weed is more likely to be found in the 'rough' or in fairways on golf courses. It is not likely to occur in lawns or greens unless these are neglected.

ERADICATION. Close mowing weakens and reduces considerably but removing with a weed-fork may have to be resorted to. Resistant to selective weed-killers.

CINQUEFOIL OR CREEPING
CINQUEFOIL

WILD TANSEY, GOOSE-
GRASS OR SILVERWEED

WILD TANSEY, GOOSE-GRASS OR SILVERWEED (*Potentilla Anserina*, Linn.). (Perennial)

BOTANICAL DESCRIPTION. Stock tufted with long creeping runners rooting at the nodes as in *P. reptans*.

Leaves pinnate with numerous oblong, deeply toothed leaflets, green on the upper side, silvery white underneath.

Peduncles long, solitary at the rooting nodes, bearing a single, rather large yellow flower.

NOTES. From the botanical description it will be noted that this weed 'rooting at the nodes' resembles in habit, the strawberry. It is very deep-rooted and not easy to control. The encouragement of a dense sward minimizes the likelihood of invasion.

ERADICATION. Raking and close mowing, weeding by hand and removal with a hand-fork are advised. Where the weed occurs in colonies, remove and returf. Resistant to selective weed-killers.

TORMENTIL (*Potentilla tormentilla*, Neck.). (Perennial)

BOTANICAL DESCRIPTION. Rootstock thick and woody. Stems erect or procumbent at the base, several times forked, more or less silky-hairy as well as the leaves.

Leaves, lower ones often shortly stalked, but the upper ones always sessile, consisting of three or rarely five deeply toothed leaflets.

Peduncles in the forks of the stem, or in the axils of the upper leaves, forming a loose, leafy terminal cyme.

Flowers small, bright yellow and mostly with four petals, the first on each stem has occasionally five.

NOTES. Occasionally found in lawns and greens but more often when these are neglected. A frequent weed of golf 'fairways' and 'rough'. Preferring light sandy soils it is usually found on heaths or moors.

ERADICATION. Susceptible to selective weed-killers.

TORMENTIL   SALAD BURNET

SALAD BURNET (*Poterium Sanguisorba*, Linn.). (Perennial)

BOTANICAL DESCRIPTION. A glabrous or slightly downy perennial, the stem seldom above a foot high.

Leaflets small, ovate, deeply toothed.

Flower heads of light green colour, very occasionally acquiring a purplish tinge. Lower flowers all males with the numerous stamens projecting into hanging tufts; upper flowers female with long style ending in purple-tufted stigma. Ripe calyx more or less distinctly quadrangular, and irregularly wrinkled and pitted.

NOTES. Offered by seedsmen as a salad herb it is found wild in limestone districts, in England, but it is scarce in Scotland and Ireland.

Occurs as a weed in the fairways of golf courses, and on lawns and sports grounds which have not been closely mown. More common on dry, calcareous soils.

ERADICATION. Close mowing, hand-weeding or removal with a weed-fork.

PARSLEY PIERT OR LADY'S MANTLE (*Alchemilla arvensis*, Scop.). (Annual)

BOTANICAL DESCRIPTION. A dwarf annual about two or three inches high, frequently flowering when only one inch high. Branched and covered with soft hairs.

Leaves fan-shaped, clasping the stem like an inverted mantle.

Flowers very minute, green and sessile, form small heads in the axils of the leaves.

PARSLEY PIERT OR LADY'S MANTLE

NOTES. A troublesome weed when established, setting seeds even when closely mown.

ERADICATION. Somewhat resistant to selective weed-killers; scarifying and hand-weeding may be necessary.

h) THE STELLATE FAMILY (*Stellateæ*, a tribe of the natural order: *Rubiaceæ*)

Rubiaceæ, of which *Stellateæ* is a tribe, is an extensive tropical order which includes such well-known plants as coffee, bouvardia and gardenia.

FIELD MADDER (*Sherardia arvensis*, Linn.). (Annual)

BOTANICAL DESCRIPTION. This prostrate annual seldom grows more than six inches high. There are usually six leaves arranged in a whorl and the lower ones are small and obovate, while those higher up are linear or lanceolate with rough edges ending in a fine point. The plant bears little heads of very small blue or pink flowers.

NOTES. Field madder is not a troublesome weed, but occasionally appears in newly sown lawns.

ERADICATION. Hand-weeding and close mowing to prevent the plants from seeding is usually sufficient.

FIELD MADDER

HEATH GALIUM OR
HEATH BEDSTRAW

HEATH GALIUM OR HEATH BEDSTRAW (*Galium saxatile* Linn.). (Perennial)

BOTANICAL DESCRIPTION. A small, much-branched perennial, often tufted at the base. The numerous flowering stems are weak, from five to six inches high and smooth at the angles.

Leaves usually six, in a whorl, sometimes more. The lower ones small and obovate, those higher up narrow and upon elongated stems, linear the edges varying, some smooth, others rough, but all ending in a small point at the tip.

The white flowers are borne profusely in short panicles. Fruits small and inclined to be granulated.

NOTES. Found in all parts of Britain, and usually occurring in open heaths and pastures. Frequent upon lawns in some districts.

ERADICATION. Does not yield readily to lawn sand but susceptible to selective weed-killers.

(i) THE SCROPHULARIA OR SPEEDWELL FAMILY (Natural order: *Scrophulariaceæ*)

Among garden plants, *Antirrhinum* and *Veronica* are perhaps the best-known members of this order. As weeds of turf they are seldom important; species of speedwell (*Veronica*) being found occasionally in established swards.

THYME-LEAVED SPEEDWELL

GERMANDER SPEEDWELL
OR BIRD'S EYE

THYME-LEAVED SPEEDWELL (*Veronica serpyllifolia*, Linn.). (Perennial)

BOTANICAL DESCRIPTION. The stems are much branched, rather woody and shortly creeping, giving the plant a decidedly tufted appearance. The flowering branches grow from two to five inches high, but in fine turf their height is much reduced. The nearly sessile ovate leaves are under half an inch long, glabrous and dark green in colour. The whole plant is glabrous. Flowers, small pale blue or sometimes white with dark streaks, sessile or shortly stalked in terminal spikes, or racemes.

NOTES. Seeds areoccasionally an impurity of mixtures of lawn grass seeds.

ERADICATION. Lawn sand is effective. Susceptible to selective weed-killers.

GERMANDER SPEEDWELL OR BIRD'S EYE (*Veronica Chamædrys*, Linn.).

BOTANICAL DESCRIPTION. A weak, creeping plant, the stem procumbent, growing a foot or more long. A characteristic which distinguishes this from other species, is the possession of two lines of hairs between each pair of leaves, upon the otherwise glabrous stems. The shortly stalked leaves are ovate-cordate, crenate and hairy.

The flowers, bright blue, half an inch across, borne on long pedicles in axillary racemes. Capsule broadest towards the top.

NOTES. This weed rarely gives trouble.

ERADICATION. Lawn sand is effective. Susceptible to selective weed-killers.

IVY-LEAVED SPEEDWELL   FIELD SPEEDWELL

IVY-LEAVED SPEEDWELL(*Veronica hederæfolia*, Linn.).(Annual)

BOTANICAL DESCRIPTION. An almost smooth annual. Leaves stalked, broadly orbicular with coarse teeth or short lobes. The calyx is an important aid to identification for the divisions are broadly heart-shaped and not narrowed at the bases.

Capsule resembles *V. agrestis* but with one or two seeds only in each cell.

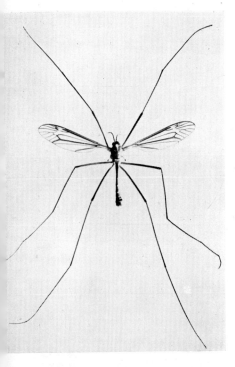

7a. Crane-Fly or Daddy-Long-legs

7b. Leather Jacket

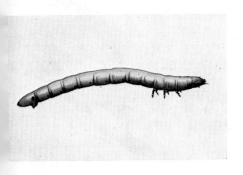

7c. Wireworm

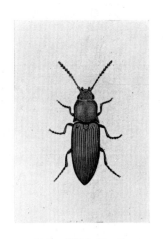

7d. Click-Beetle

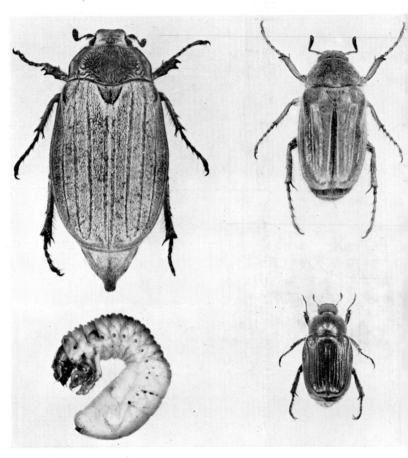

8. June Bug

Notes. Not likely to be found in established turf. Often appears in newly sown swards.

Eradication. Cannot withstand close mowing. Hand-weeding in seedling turf usually sufficient.

FIELD SPEEDWELL (*Veronica agrestis*, Linn.). (Annual)

Botanical Description. A more hairy species than *V. hederae-folia*, with procumbent stems growing about a foot long. Leaves less distinctly stalked than the foregoing, those lower down opposite, the remainder mostly alternate each with a flower in its axil. Flowers blue or pinkish white. Divisions of calyx ovate or oblong; longer than the corolla in most plants.

Capsule has two ovoid erect lobes with small number of seeds in each.

Notes. Not a weed of great significance, may occur in newly sown turf.

Eradication. Same as for the germander speedwell.

WALL SPEEDWELL OR CORN SPEEDWELL

WALL SPEEDWELL OR CORN SPEEDWELL (*Veronica arvensis*, Linn.). (Annual)

Botanical Description. A low-growing hairy annual, rarely exceeding a height of six inches. The habit is variable with stems erect or branched at the base. The leaves opposite, ovate and toothed, with the exception of the upper ones, which are smaller, alternate and lanceolate,

G   97

Flowers small, blue or nearly white. Capsule, broad, much flattened.

NOTES. Can be an impurity of lawn grass seeds, and may appear in seedling turf. Common in wheat and clover crops.

ERADICATION. Purchase lawn grass seeds only from a reliable seedsman; avoid so-called 'cheap' mixtures. Resistant to lawn sand, but spraying or dusting with selective weed-killers has been found effective when it has invaded established lawns. Hand-weeding on newly sown swards usually sufficient.

(i) THE GERANIUM FAMILY (Natural order: *Geraniaceæ*)

The cape Pelargoniums used for greenhouse and garden decoration belong to this family while the common Nasturtium is a close ally.

DOVE'S-FOOT GERANIUM OR
SOFT CRANESBILL

COMMON ERODIUM

DOVE'S FOOT GERANIUM OR SOFT CRANESBILL (*Geranium molle*, Linn.). (Annual or Biennial)

BOTANICAL DESCRIPTION. Annual, often tufted at the base, more or less covered with rather long, soft, spreading hairs, the stems weak and spreading, very short when first flowering and seldom attaining a foot.

Radical leaves numerous on very long stalks, orbicular, rather above an inch in diameter, divided to below the middle into seven to eleven obovate or wedge-shaped lobes, which are again three- or five-lobed. The upper leaves few, small, with fewer but deeper and narrow divisions.

Peduncles shorter than the leaves, each with two small purplish flowers, the sepals obtuse or scarcely pointed, the petals deeply notched, scarcely longer than the calyx.

Carpels usually distinctly marked with transverse wrinkles. Seeds quite smooth, about one-twentieth of an inch long, oval-cylindrical, light chocolate-brown in colour.

NOTES. This is a widespread weed in lawn turf on all types of soil.

When the turf is mown closely at all times, it rarely appears but on football pitches, cricket outfields, and golf fairways, where the grasses are not mown so closely, it is usually in evidence.

Sometimes confused with the erodiums, a description of which follows, but can be distinguished by examining the flower. These have three stamens where there are five in the erodiums. The leaves of geraniums are palmate, of erodiums pinnate.

ERADICATION. Turf fed well is not likely to become infested. Close mowing and hand-weeding or forking before the seeds are set is advised. Susceptible to selective weed-killers.

COMMON ERODIUM (*Erodium cicutarium*, L'Hér.). (Annual)

BOTANICAL DESCRIPTION. An annual often forming a dense tuft with a thick tap root which, in some places, lasts into the second year. More or less covered with spreading hairs, which are sometimes viscid.

Stems are sometimes exceedingly short, often lengthening to six inches or nearly a foot.

Leaves mostly radical, pinnate, on long stalks; the segments distinct and deeply pinnatifid, with narrow more or less cut lobes.

Peduncles, erect, bearing an umbel of from two or three to ten or twelve small purplish or pink flowers. Sepals pointed, about the length of the obovate entire petals. Carpels slightly hairy.

NOTES. Not likely to occur in turf which is mown frequently, but may be found on neglected lawns, golf fairways, and sports grounds, on a variety of soils, but more frequently near the seaside.

ERADICATION. Same as for dove's foot geranium.

MUSK ERODIUM (*Erodium moschatum*, L'Hér.). (Annual)

BOTANICAL DESCRIPTION. A larger and coarser plant than *E. cicutarium*, often smelling strongly of musk. Stems sometimes a foot long. Leaves on long footstalks with from nine to eleven distinct, ovate segments or leaflets, often cordate at the base and deeply toothed or shortly pinnatifid. Flowers generally numerous in the umbel and of a bluish purple. Usually larger than *E. cicutarium*. Peduncles sometimes six or eight inches long.

NOTES. Found mostly in sandy places, near to the sea, particularly in the West of England, and South Wales; but it is not common. It is more abundant in the Channel Islands.

ERADICATION. Same as for dove's foot geranium.

MUSK ERODIUM

SEA ERODIUM OR
SEA STORK'S-BILL

SEA ERODIUM OR SEA STORK'S-BILL (*Erodium maritimum*, L'Hér.). (Annual)

BOTANICAL DESCRIPTION. A small, hairy annual. In habit similar to *E. cicutarium*, but distinguished by its simple, not pinnate, leaves which are often not more than half an inch long and ovate-cordate, more or less toothed and sometimes lobed, but seldom beyond half an inch to the midribs. Peduncles not often longer than the leaves, with one or two and occasionally more small reddish-purple flowers. The beak to the fruit is much smaller than in the species described previously.

NOTES. Not a common weed. As its name suggests, it is found near the seaside, more often on the south and west coasts of England, up to the south of Scotland and all round the Irish coasts. It is now and then discovered inland upon the lighter soils.

ERADICATION. Same as for dove's foot geranium.

(j) THE GOOSEFOOT FAMILY (Natural order: *Chenopodiaceæ*)

SALTWORT (*Salsola Kali*, Linn.). (Annual)

BOTANICAL DESCRIPTION. A procumbent glabrous annual, the stems hard and very branched, six inches to nearly a foot long.

Leaves all ending in a stout prickle, the lower ones semi-cylindrical, linear, slightly enlarged at the base, the uppermost shorter and broader and nearly triangular. Flowers sessile in the upper axils.

NOTES. This weed is found frequently on the coasts of England, Ireland and Scotland in maritime sands and sea marches, but it is not a frequent weed of turf except in the 'rough' of seaside golf courses.

ERADICATION. Close mowing and hand-weeding or 'grubbing' with a weed-fork should suffice.

FAT HEN OR WHITE GOOSEFOOT

WILD BEET

FAT HEN OR WHITE GOOSEFOOT (*Chenopodium album*, Linn.). (Annual)

BOTANICAL DESCRIPTION. An erect annual growing from one to three feet high, of a pale green or nearly white colour.

Leaves stalked, the lower ones ovate or broadly lanceolate, sinuately toothed or angular, those higher up narrow and entire.

Flowers in clusters and in short axillary spikes. Fruit enclosed in the perianth.

101

NOTES. This is not a weed found in closely mown turf, but very frequent in newly sown lawns.

ERADICATION. Hand-weeding is usually all that is necessary. Susceptible to selective weed-killers.

WILD BEET (*Beta maritima*, Linn.). (Perennial)

BOTANICAL DESCRIPTION. Stock, short, hard and of a few years' duration. Stems erect or spreading and branched. Height about two feet.

Leaves, the lower ones large, broad, thick and green, the upper ones small and narrow.

Flowers, green, single or clustered in long, loose terminal spikes, often branching into a leafy panicle.

The perianth, when ripe, forms a hard, angular and often prickly mass, enclosing a single horizontal seed.

NOTES. A seashore plant often found on the coasts of Britain, south of Fife and Argyll.

The garden beets and the farm mangolds are cultivated varieties.

Seldom occurs in turf, except near the seaside—particularly in sandy or marshy types of land.

ERADICATION. Cannot withstand close mowing. Hand-weeding or 'grubbing' with a hand-fork usually sufficient.

ANNUAL KNAWEL

KNOTWEED OR KNOTGRASS

ANNUAL KNAWEL (*Scleranthus annuus*, Linn.). (Annual)

BOTANICAL DESCRIPTION. A spreading branched annual, two to three inches high, slightly downy or glabrous.

Leaves very narrow. Calyx becomes enlarged after flowering, the narrow lobes pointed, stiff and erect.

NOTES. This weed usually occurs on light sandy soils. It is fairly common in England, Ireland and southern Scotland, but less frequent farther north.

If it is allowed to become established, it quickly smothers the fine grasses.

ERADICATION. Raking and scarifying and hand-weeding and lifting with a weed-fork are recommended.

(k) THE POLYGONUM FAMILY (Natural order: *Polygonaceæ*)

The garden rhubarbs are members of this order which contains a number of common turf weeds.

KNOTWEED OR KNOTGRASS (*Polygonum aviculare*, Linn.).
(Annual)

BOTANICAL DESCRIPTION. A much-branched, wiry, prostrate annual, more erect when growing among the grasses. Often from one to two feet long. Stipules white and scarious, becoming ragged at the edges. Leaves rarely more than an inch long, narrow—oblong in shape.

Flowers, small, in clusters of two to five, shortly stalked and in the axils of most of the leaves. The branches vary, some very long and slender with the leaves far apart, others short and densely matted, with the small leaves crowded together.

Fruiting perianths small, the segments white on the edge, green in the centre.

Nuts, triangular, seldom exceeding the perianth, not shining, but minutely granulated or wrinkled.

NOTES. This is a very tough-stemmed weed, with a deep taproot, which assists the plant to survive at the expense of the dwarf grasses, during periods of dry weather.

A common weed on football pitches, particularly in goalmouth areas. Likely to appear wherever the soil is consolidated excessively.

ERADICATION. Hand-weeding on small areas. On larger areas raking up, followed by cutting is recommended. Somewhat susceptible to selective weed-killers and two or more applications may be necessary.

BROAD DOCK OR COMMON DOCK (*Rumex obtusifolius*, Linn.). (Perennial)

BOTANICAL DESCRIPTION. Stem, slightly branched, two to three feet high, resembles *R. crispus* but differs in its broader leaves, the radical ones often nine inches by four inches, rounded at the top and cordate at the bases, the upper ones narrow and more pointed. It also differs in the flowers which are borne in looser and more distinct whorls with the panicles less crowded.

The inner segments of the perianth although often broadly ovate, are never cordate and are bordered below the middle by a few small teeth, usually ending in a fine point.

NOTES. Docks are not usually troublesome in established turf, but this species and the curled dock (*R. crispus*, Linn.) which it closely resembles, except for the differences described above, sometimes occur in newly sown lawns and sports grounds.

ERADICATION. Very susceptible to selective weed-killers.

BROAD DOCK

SHEEP SORREL (*Rumex Acetosella*, Linn.). (Perennial)

BOTANICAL DESCRIPTION. Plant slender, from three to four inches high, but often reaching one foot. Acid to the taste. Stems wiry, creeping and reddish in colour. Leaves narrow, lanceloate and linear, a large number sagittate, the lobes of the base usually spreading and often divided.

Flowers, small, dioecious, green turning red, in slender terminal panicles.

Segments of the perianth small, broadly ovate or orbicular, entire and thin; the inner ones closing over the triangular nut.

NOTES. The seeds of this weed are often an impurity of lawn grass seeds. Very prevalent in dry situations and its presence indicates that the soil is sour and deficient in lime. It also thrives where the soil is loose, whereas compression tends to suppress it.

ERADICATION. As for common or broad dock.

SORREL DOCK, COMMON SORREL OR SOUR DOCK
(*Rumex Acetosa*, Linn.). (Perennial)

BOTANICAL DESCRIPTION. Grows one to two feet high. Leaves chiefly radical, oblong, three to five inches long and larger than *R*.

SHEEP SORREL

SORREL DOCK

acetosella, sagittate at the base with broad, pointed auricles, brigh green and very acid; the stem leaves few on shorter stalks. Flowers dioecious or sometimes manoecious in long terminal, leafless panicles, usually turning red. Inner segments of the fruiting perianth enlarged, orbicular, thick and almost petal-like.

NOTES. The leaves of this common weed of wet pastures are sometimes used for salads. This species differs from the sheep sorrel and can be recognized by its broader leaves which have no 'ears'. It seldom appears in turf and causes little trouble.

ERADICATION. Same as for sheep sorrel.

(l) THE RANUNCULUS FAMILY (Natural order: *Ranunculaceæ*)

The most troublesome members of this family in turf are the buttercups, common weeds of pastures and lawns.

COMMON BUTTERCUP OR CROWFOOT (*Ranunculus acris*). (Perennial)

BOTANICAL DESCRIPTION. A perennial which varies and which is more or less covered with soft hairs, mostly spreading but deflexed on the lower part of the stem.

The leaves are nearly all stalked and deeply divided into three, five or seven palmate segments.

Flowers, rather large, bright yellow on long stalks. Sepals, yellowish-green, concave but not reflexed on the peduncle.

NOTES. A very abundant weed found on a great variety of soils, but more frequent where moist conditions prevail.

ERADICATION. Eliminated by applications of selective weed-killers.

COMMON BUTTERCUP   CREEPING BUTTERCUP

CREEPING BUTTERCUP (*Ranunculus repens*, Linn.). (Perennial)

BOTANICAL DESCRIPTION. Flowers identical with *R. acris*, but runners shoot out from among the radical leaves, and new plants are formed and root at every node. The flower stems are seldom a foot high, the leaves divided into three stalked segments, each one lobed and toothed, the central one projecting considerably beyond the other, giving the leaf an ovate form as distinct from the rounded leaf of *R. acris*.

NOTES. This species is very aggressive. Its creeping habit and power to root at the nodes, like a strawberry, enable it to spread rapidly.

ERADICATION. Susceptible to selective weed-killers.

BULBOUS BUTTERCUP (*Ranunculus bulbosus*, Linn.). (Perennial)

BOTANICAL DESCRIPTION. A hairy erect perennial having a bulbous base to its stem. Leaves smaller than in *R. repens* and distinguished from it by reflexed sepals touching the stem, but in this respect it resembles an annual species, *R. hirsutus*.

Flowers, yellow. Carpels with a series of tubercles within the broad margin.

NOTES. A common golf course weed on sandy and calcareous soils, most conspicuous from April until August when in flower.

ERADICATION. Less susceptible to selective weed-killers, two or more applications may be required.

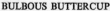

BULBOUS BUTTERCUP   LESSER CELANDINE

LESSER CELANDINE OR FIGWORT (*Ranunculus Ficaria*, Linn.). (Perennial)

BOTANICAL DESCRIPTION. Small root-stalk produces a number of oblong or cylindrical tubers, each one capable of becoming a perfect plant.

Leaves mostly radical, cordate, obtuse or crenate, thick, shining and smooth.

Flower stems a little longer than the radical leaves, bearing a single flower.

NOTES. This weed is common in Britain, but is less often found in the West Highlands of Scotland.

ERADICATION. As for common buttercup.

(m) THE UMBELLATE FAMILY (Natural order: *Umbelliferæ*)

The wild carrot is the only member of this family to cause trouble in fine turf.

WILD OR COMMON CARROT (*Daucus Carota*, Linn.). (Annual or Biennial)

BOTANICAL DESCRIPTION. This erect annual or biennial forms a tap root. The leaves are twice or thrice pinnate, with deeply lobed pinnatifid segments, lanceolate or linear, sometimes short and crenate.

Umbels terminal, rather large with numerous crowded rays, the inner ones very short, the outer much longer and after flowering a globular form is assumed by the closing over of the outer rays.

Fruit covered with prickles.

NOTES. Not a weed which is likely to be found frequently, but it is fairly common in fields and pastures, chiefly on dry calcareous and loamy soils.

ERADICATION. Hand-weeding usually sufficient.

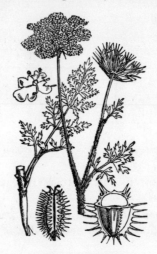

WILD CARROT

(n) THE CRUCIFER FAMILY (Natural order: *Cruciferæ*)

The characters of the family are well defined in the flowers which have four petals arranged in the form of a cross, hence its name ('crux'—cross: 'fere'—to bear).

SHEPHERD'S PURSE (*Capsella Bursa-pastoris*, Medith). (Annual)

BOTANICAL DESCRIPTION. Root tapering, often to a great depth. Radical leaves in form of rosette, pinnatifid, with larger ovate or triangular terminal lobes, or sometimes entire.

Stem erect, from a few inches to above a foot high, rather rough and often hairy, with a few oblong or lanceolate entire or toothed leaves, clasping the stem from projecting auricles. Pods in a long loose raceme, usually triangular, truncate at the top, with the angles slightly rounded and base narrowed, sometimes notched at the top and almost obcordate. Seeds ten to twelve in each cell.

NOTES. Seeds can lie dormant in the soil for many years and then germinate when conditions are favourable, invading newly sown lawns.

ERADICATION. Hand-weeding and close mowing are usually sufficient. Responds readily to lawn sand. Very susceptible to selective weed-killers.

WHITLOW GRASS (*Draba verna*, Linn.). (Annual)

BOTANICAL DESCRIPTION. A dwarf annual of only a few weeks' duration, the leaves all radical, ovate or oblong, seldom above half an inch long and closely spreading on the ground. Peduncles slender, erect, one to three or rarely four inches long. Petals small, white and

SHEPHERD'S PURSE

WHITLOW GRASS

deeply cleft. Pods on rather long, slender pedicles containing numerous minute seeds.

NOTES. During the summer whitlow grass dies out and therefore it cannot be regarded as a dangerous turf weed. It is most common on lawns on sandy soil and frequently makes its appearance in seedling turf.

ERADICATION. Hand-weeding and close mowing are usually sufficient.

CHARLOCK OR WILD MUSTARD (*Brassica sinapis*, Visiani) (Annual)

BOTANICAL DESCRIPTION. A coarse annual with stiff, spreading hairs, it usually grows from one to two feet high.

The lower leaves usually with one large oval or oblong coarsely toothed segment and a few smaller ones along the leafstalk. Flowers, rather large. Pods more or less spreading, half to one and a half inches long, of which rather more than a third is occupied by a stout beak often containing a seed in its base; the valves glabrous or rough with stiff reflexed hairs.

NOTES. This is a familiar weed of arable land but gardeners and green-keepers are most likely to find it in the seedling stage when the cotyle-dons resemble those of a seedling turnip.

ERADICATION. Hand-weeding is all that is necessary.

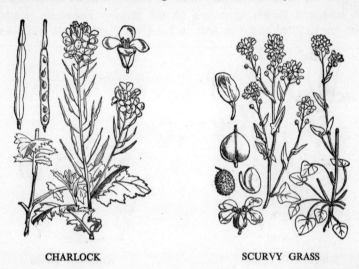

CHARLOCK   SCURVY GRASS

SCURVY GRASS (*Cochlearia officinalis*, Linn.). (Annual or Biennial)

BOTANICAL DESCRIPTION. A low-growing, glabrous fleshy annual or biennial with stems seldom more than six inches long. Leaves vary much in size and shape. The lower ones stalked, orbicular deltoid or reniform, entire or angularly toothed; the upper ones sometimes similar, some-times ovate or oblong and often quite sessile. Flowers in short racemes, the petals obovate and spreading. Pods globular or ovoid.

NOTES. Not uncommon on seashores in England and Ireland, but more abundant in Scotland, where it also occurs on the margins of some rivers.

Frequently introduced with sea-washed turf, and is fairly common on bowling greens.

ERADICATION. Grubbing with a weed-fork during wet weather.

(o) THE PLUMBAGO FAMILY (Natural order: *Plumbagineæ*)

A species of *Ameria*, known as common thrift or sea pink, is the only member of this family to cause trouble in lawns.

THRIFT OR SEA PINK (*Armeria vulgaris*, Willd.; *Armeria maritima*, Willd.). (Perennial)

BOTANICAL DESCRIPTION. The stocks form perennial tufts with numerous radical leaves, all narrow linear, entire with a single prominent midrib.

THRIFT   SALTWORT

Flowering stems single and leafless, glabrous or shortly downy, three to four inches, to twice that height, each bearing a globular head of pink or sometimes white flowers; the petal-like border of the calyx crowned by very short slender teeth.

NOTES. This plant prefers the seaside but will grow inland and is often introduced when sea-washed turf is laid.

ERADICATION. Sea-washed turf should be examined before laying and the weeds carefully removed. Susceptible to selective weed-killers.

(p) THE PRIMROSE FAMILY (Natural order: *Primulaceae*)

A single species of the genus Glaux is often a weed of fine turf.

SEA-MILKWORT, BLACK SALTWORT (*Glaux maritima*, Linn.). (Perennial)

BOTANICAL DESCRIPTION. A decumbent fleshy marine perennial

111

from three to six inches high, growing in patches with numerous ovate glaucous leaves. Flowers, pale pink, axillary.

NOTES. In nature it is found on salt marshes and sands near to the sea and is often a weed of sea-washed turf.

ERADICATION. Susceptible to selective weed-killers but two applications may be required.

(q) THE RUSH FAMILY (Natural order: *Juncaceæ*)

One of the woodrushes, a species of *Luzula*, is sometimes found as a weed in fine turf.

FIELD WOODRUSH   ANNUAL MEADOW-GRASS

FIELD WOODRUSH (*Luzula campestris,* Br.). (Perennial)

BOTANICAL DESCRIPTION. Stock branched and tufted with creeping offsets. Stems slender, erect, six inches to a foot high. Leaves chiefly radical or near the base of the stem linear and grass-like, two or three inches long, more or less fringed with long white hairs.

Flowers collected six or eight or more together in close ovoid heads or clusters, of which from three to six form a terminal panicle; the central cluster sessile, the others on slender peduncles varying in length. Perianth segments very pointed, brown, with light-coloured shining edges. Capsules, short and obtuse.

NOTES. This plant grows wild in dry pastures, heaths and woods, and occasionally appears in lawns and greens.

ERADICATION. Resistant to selective weed-killers and lawn sand. Hand-weeding is usually resorted to.

(r) THE GRASS FAMILY (Natural order: *Gramineæ*)

It is strange to discuss any member of this family as a weed of turf, yet here we have another of our values reversed, for grasses, components of prescriptions of grasses and clovers for permanent pasture and leys, are found among our weeds of fine turf.

ANNUAL MEADOW-GRASS (*Poa annua*, Linn.). (Annual)

BOTANICAL DESCRIPTION. Tufted, usually about six inches high, with flat, flaccid bright green leaves. Panicle loose and spreading one and a half to three inches long, with slender branches. Spikelets all stalked, oblong or linear, each with from three to six or rarely more, flowers. Flowering glumes scarious at the top. Keeled from the base; the lateral nerves also slightly prominent when dry, without woolly hairs on the axis of the spikelet, but very minutely silky on the keel.

NOTES. As a weed of bowling greens and other fine turf it gives a great deal of trouble. It is probably the commonest of all grasses and grows readily between stones and on the sides of garden paths.

In America the name 'Pavement Grass' has been given to it.

In this country it is often a leading constituent of the grasses forming the turf in city parks and is very common in London.

Fine turf may often become poor and thin during periods of prolonged dry weather, but *P. annua* survives and usurps the accepted lawn species. Its use as an ingredient in prescriptions for lawns and sports grounds has often been advocated, but seeds reaching a reasonable standard of purity are difficult to obtain commercially.

When found in small patches or tufts on bowling or putting greens an uneven surface is noticeable and *P. annua* rapidly establishes itself in newly laid sea-washed turf.

ERADICATION. Hand-weeding in the early stages may keep the grass under control, but where a sward is suffering from a serious invasion, spraying with arsenic acid at the strength of 1 in 80 is recommended at the rate of one gallon to twenty square yards.

In America monthly applications of lead arsenate in the spring at the rate of 5 lb. per 100 square feet have been found beneficial for they appeared to encourage the growth of the more desirable grasses, which crowded out the usurper.

The application of common salt at the rate of 1 oz. to the square yard is also suggested, applications being made in spring, summer, autumn.

COCK'S-FOOT (*Dactylis glomerata*, Linn.). (Perennial)

DESCRIPTION. The plant forms coarse tufts, the leaves are broad and fan out from the roots. They are light green to bluish in colour, folded in the flattened shoot; the upper surface ribless, hairless, but rough. Sheaths, compressed, keeled on both sides. Flowering head a panicle of spikelets, the lobes giving the effect of a bird's foot. Seeds light coloured, ending in a curved point.

NOTES. A very unsightly lawn weed owing to its tufted habit and broad leaves. Often confused with Yorkshire Fog (*Holcus lanatus*) but

COCK'S-FOOT

'fog' is hairy and the leaves rolled in the bud, not folded. Common on all types of soil.

ERADICATION. Where possible, remove the whole plant with a hand-fork. If colonized, lift the turves and replace with weed-free turf.

Slashing with a knife and close mowing are also recommended.

YORKSHIRE FOG (*Holcus lanatus*, Linn.). (Perennial)

DESCRIPTION. A tufted grass with a creeping rootstock. Stems and leaves covered with very short down or hairs which gives the plant a soft appearance. The leaves are rolled in the shoot and the veins of the basal sheath are pink.

The flowering head is a panicle and is cream coloured or has a tinge of pink. The fruit enclosed in glumes is glossy.

NOTES. Where the soil is moist, this is a common lawn weed and one which is often an impurity of lawn grass seeds.

ERADICATION. Systematic slashing with a knife and close mowing will reduce and finally destroy.

CREEPING SOFT GRASS OR SOFT HOLCUS (*Holcus mollis*, Linn.). (Perennial)

BOTANICAL DESCRIPTION. Resembles very closely Yorkshire Fog and some botanists consider it to be a variety and not a distinct species. It can be distinguished, however, by its strong underground stems and it is not usually so downy, although the hairs on the knots of the flowering stems are generally more conspicuous.

NOTES. Occurs as an impurity of lawn grass seeds.

ERADICATION. Removing with a hand-fork, taking care to dig out the underground stems.

CREEPING SOFT GRASS

SWEET VERNAL

SWEET VERNAL OR VERNAL GRASS (*Anthoxanthum odoratum*, Linn.). (Perennial)

DESCRIPTION. Erect perennial, quite glabrous, growing in compact tufts. Flowering head a spike-like panicle. Awned seeds dark chocolate-brown. Has a fragrant smell when bruised.

NOTES. This is a widespread species but appears to prefer the drier soils. Seeds are sometimes included in prescriptions for mowing simply because of its sweet, 'hay-like' smell.

ERADICATION. Where it has colonized it should be cut and new turf laid. Single plants can be removed with a hand-fork. Slashing with a knife and close mowing will often destroy.

COUCH OR QUITCH OR TWITCH (*Agropyrum repens*, Beauv.). (Perennial)

BOTANICAL DESCRIPTION. The rootstock creeps extensively and produces leaves and roots at each 'knot' of the whole plant, varying

COUCH   WALL BARLEY

from a bright green to a pale glaucous colour. Flowering stems one to two or even three feet high. Leaves almost ribless but rough when rubbed from top to bottom. There are prominent 'ears' at the base of each leaf. Inflorescence a spike with eight to ten or more spikelets. In general appearance these can be said to resemble rye-grass, but whereas in the latter the backs of the seeds are towards the stem, in this species the sides of the 'seeds' are nearest to the stem.

NOTES. This weed is the 'gardener's nightmare' for if the underground rhizome is broken, each part can produce a new plant. It is found on all soils but perhaps more abundant on light soil.

ERADICATION. Where troublesome thorough fallowing is essential prior to sowing seeds. Hand-forking is advised where small areas have to be dealt with and the plant will usually succumb to continuous close mowing. For larger areas which are densely colonized an application of sodium chlorate in September is recommended; broadcasting at the rate of 2 cwt. per acre, but when this application is made sowing should be delayed for as long as possible. Six months or more are, however, normally safe.

WALL BARLEY GRASS OR WAYBENT (*Hordeum murinum*, Linn.). (Annual)

BOTANICAL DESCRIPTION. A rather coarse tufted grass. Stems decumbent at the base. One to two feet long. Leaves often hairy. Spike dense and cylindrical, three or four inches long, thickly beset with long rough awns.

NOTES. This weed is seldom met with on garden lawns but occurs on sports grounds, on dry soils, and by footpaths, roadsides, and waste places.

ERADICATION. Well-fed turf on good well-watered soil is not likely to show signs of wall barley grass. Cutting before seeding and close mowing will eradicate.

(s) MOSSES (*Ceratodon purpureus*, Brid.; *Bryum argenteum*, Hedw.; *Hypnum cupressiforme*, Hedw.; *Polytrichum juniperinum*, Willd.; *Barbula convoluta*, Hedw.)

Moss control is essential if the finest quality turf is to be maintained. There are probably nine mosses which infest fine turf. Those which are most common are named above.

Why does moss occur in lawns? Various reasons are given—bad drainage, consolidation, lack of lime, acidity and impoverishment being the most general. Consolidation is sometimes necessary to counteract a loose fluffy surface where moss abounds and, on the other hand, spiking and scarifying may be required where the surface is 'capped' or 'hidebound'.

Dawson[1] states that mowing plays an important part for grasses cut to a length of $\frac{1}{4}$ in. are less infested with moss than those cut to $\frac{1}{8}$ in. Mosses need light which a closely mown sward provides.

The question of alkalinity or acidity is a vexed one, but as moss grows freely in both acid and alkaline soils, the subject is not of paramount importance.

Low fertility is perhaps the crux of the problem, and this can be

[1] Dawson, R. B.: *Journal, Board of Greenkeeping Research.*

brought about by bad drainage, consolidation, lack of lime (in certain cases) and acidity (when excessive). If soil is rendered more fertile, by correcting bad drainage, rolling where required, spiking and scarifying, and by the judicious use of fertilizers, moss is not likely to be troublesome, once it has been destroyed.

The usual method of moss destruction is by applications of sulphate of iron, usually in the form of lawn sand, and when moss has been 'burned off' to maintain fertility by using composts and manures.

Permanganate of potash applied in solution or in dry form at the rate of 1 oz. to 3 square yards reduces moss, but its reappearance indicates that merely treating with permanganate of potash is insufficient.

For moss control the following treatment is recommended.

Examine the turf to ascertain whether the surface soil is loose and 'fluffy', or hidebound. If drainage is faulty, take steps to improve it. If the soil is loose, consolidate with a light roller when the sward is dry, but if it is hidebound or 'capped' provide aeration by forking.

Apply lawn sand at the rate of 4 oz. to the square yard to the whole of the lawn or treat the moss with permanganate of potash in dry form at 1 oz. to 3 square yards. When the moss has been 'burned off', rake the turf vigorously with a 'Springbok' or iron-pronged rake, top-dress with fertile, sifted, top-spit soil, sow lawn grass seeds at the rate of 2 oz. to the square yard.

The use of calomel[1] has been suggested for moss control. Recent experiments show that the incorporation of mercury compounds such as calomel with the usual types of lawn sand would result in the elimination of moss for at least twelve months. As moss reappeared on trial plots treated with ordinary lawn sands, within six months, the use of calomel is likely to influence control methods. Long-term experimental work is proceeding.

[1] Wyatt, Frank M.: *Gardener's Chronicle*. No. 3253, Vol. CXXV.

Chapter Ten

Weed Control

꙳꙳꙳꙳ ◦ ꙳꙳꙳꙳

Earlier discussion on fallowing, soil pre-treatment, and the application of selective weed-killers and lawn sand to established turf, reveals that there are two phases in the control of weeds: inhibition and elimination.

It will have been noted that fertilizers play a most important part in the maintenance of lawn turf and that weed control is influenced not only by the chemical composition of the soil, but also by its physical condition. Likewise, mowing, rolling, aeration, watering and the weakening of weed colonies by 'slashing' with a knife have a part to play.

Chemical Weed Control

It is agreed that lawn grasses, particularly species of *Festuca* (fescues) and *Agrostis* (bents) can withstand a degree of acidity which inhibits lawn weeds. Accordingly, as applications of lime tend to increase the weed population of lawn turf the use of lime in lawn turf maintenance is restricted. Basic slag, rightly regarded as a valuable fertilizer for agricultural grassland, is not held in such high favour for lawn turf, as the improvement of pastures is usually brought about by an increase in the growth of the clovers. In fact, so marked is the production of clovers following an application that in earlier days many farmers were convinced that the fertilizer contained clover seeds.

1. SULPHATE OF AMMONIA AND SULPHATE OF IRON

As a fertilizer sulphate of ammonia has considerable value if used judiciously, but prior to the introduction of selective weed-killers sulphate of ammonia was probably the most important chemical agent for weed destruction. Sulphate of iron with sulphate of ammonia are the active ingredients of lawn sand and while the latter alone reduces invasion from such weeds as creeping buttercup, wild white clover, daisy, pearlwort, plantain and yarrow, it is interesting to compare their combined effects. Certain weeds, notably pearlwort and mouse-ear chick-

119

WEED CONTROL

weed, tend to increase when treated with sulphate of ammonia. It is suggested[1] that this is due to their partiality for sulphates and resistance to ammonia poisoning. Sulphate of iron is more successful in eliminating these weeds and increasing the vigour of the fine grasses. In addition to its value as a chemical weed eliminator, sulphate of iron has a beneficial effect in flocculating clay soils, although results in all cases are not completely successful. The absence of lime dressings to lawn turf often leads to conditions in which sulphate of iron can be of great value. An improvement in the colour of lawn grasses normally follows application and there is evidence that dressing with one part sulphate of iron and three parts sand, broadcasting at the rate of 4 oz. per square yard, encourages the development of Chewing's and creeping red fescue. The main weed-killing properties of sulphate of ammonia and sulphate of iron would appear to be due to their 'corrosive' action upon the broad-leaved weeds. When broadcast applications are made the weeds with a larger leaf area and less upright habit of growth retain a larger proportion of the dressing. Osmotic action is set up and the weed is 'burned' by the extraction of liquids from its cells. It will be appreciated that the effectiveness of lawn sand is dependent upon uniformity of application and favourable climatic conditions, for if rain follows treatment the 'sand' is washed from the leaves.

2. ARSENIC ACID

A dilution of liquid arsenic acid, 1 gallon to 40 gallons of water, has proved effective for the 'spot' treatment of individual weeds, but the introduction of selective weed-killers would appear to have superseded spraying, with the liquid diluted 1 in 80 or 1 in 120 for general weed suppression.

3. SODIUM CHLORATE

For weed control of paths and drives sodium chlorate enjoys wide popularity. It should not be applied to lawn weeds except for 'spot' treatment when a 10 per cent solution is suggested, but the danger to the sward from using this preparation is emphasized. It should be regarded as a last resort when other methods fail. On no account should it be broadcast over established turf.

4. SULPHURIC ACID

A dangerous poisonous acid occasionally used as a 20 per cent solution for 'spot' treatment.

[1] Cole, S. W.: *Journal of Board of Greenkeeping Research.*

5. CREOSOTE

Injection of a 20 per cent solution to individual weeds is recommended. The maximum effect appears to be obtained if used on a dry sunny day.

6. SELECTIVE WEED-KILLERS

The use of synthetic growth-regulating substances has been common agricultural and horticultural practice for many years. The more rapid rooting of cuttings, the setting of tomatoes, and the control of fruit-shedding on apple and pear trees are examples of the uses of these growth-regulating, or as they are sometimes called, 'hormone' substances. More recently, Hortomone A, alpha-naphthalene-acetic acid used at 100 parts per million, has been applied to seed potatoes to inhibit sprouting and as the same synthetic growth-regulating substance used at 10 p.p.m. will stimulate root formation, an illustration is provided of the importance of using at the rates advised by the manufacturers. In 1940 it was discovered[1] that 10–25 lb. per acre of alpha-naphthyl-acetic acid applied to a mixed sowing of oats and charlock reduced the germination of the charlock without affecting the oats. An entirely new field of weed control was opened up and in 1941 it was shown at Jealotts Hill Research Station that many growth-regulating substances possessed greater activity than alpha-naphthyl-acetic acid; thus M.C.P.A. or Methoxone (4 chloro-2 methly-phenoxy-acetic acid) was introduced followed in 1942 by 2-4-D or D.C.P.A. from the Boyce-Thomson Institute in America. The name is an abbreviation for 2: 4-dichlorophenoxyacetic acid. Selective weed-killers are available in liquid or powder forms and full directions for use are supplied by the manufacturers. Liquids are normally sprayed or 'watered' on to the turf.

RELATIVE SUSCEPTIBILITY

While all lawn weeds are affected by the selective weed-killers there is marked variation in the effects of these growth regulating substances upon the many species. Accordingly, the common weeds of lawn turf may be divided into three groups as follows:

GROUP 1. Very susceptible.

  Cat's ear (*Hypochœris radicata*)
  Creeping Buttercup (*Ranunculus repens*)
  Dandelion (*Taraxacum dens-leonis*)

[1] Hall, T. D.: *Parks, Golf Courses and Sports Grounds.*

Dock (*Rumex obtusifolium*)
Eyebright (*Euphrasia officinalis*)
Hawkbit (*Leontodon Hirtus*)
Hawkweed (*Hieracium Pilosella*)
Heath Bedstraw (*Galium saxatile*)
Lady's Mantle (*Alchemilla vulgatum*)
Mouse-ear Chickweed (*Cerastium vulgatum*)
Ox-eye Daisy (*Chrysanthemum Leucanthemum*)
Plantains (*Plantago spp.*)
Thrift (*Armeria maritima*)
Self Heal (*Prunella vulgaris*)
Sheep's Sorrel (*Rumex Acetosella*)
Shepherd's Purse (*Capsella Bursa-pastoris*)
Tormentil (*Potentilla Tormentilla*)

These weeds are normally eliminated by one application under favourable conditions.

GROUP 2. Less susceptible.
Bird's Foot Trefoil (*Lotus corniculatus*)
Bulbous Buttercup (*Ranunculus bulbosus*)
Clover (wild white) (*Trifolium repens*)
Clover (yellow suckling) (*Trifolium minus*)
Daisy (*Bellis perennis*)
Knapweed (*Centaurea nigra*)
Knotgrass (*Polygonum aviculare*)
Parsley piert (*Alchemilla arvensis*)
Sea Milkwort (*Glaux maritima*)
Thistles (*Cirsium spp.*)

These weeds are greatly reduced in number by one application and under favourable conditions elimination is possible. Normally a second application after an interval of approximately six weeks is recommended to reduce further the number of those weeds surviving.

GROUP 3. Resistant.
Mosses
Pearlwort (*Sagina procumbens*)
Silverweed (*Potentilla Anserina*)
Woodrush (*Luzula campestris*)
Yarrow (*Achillea Millefolium*)

Whilst pearlwort is classed as resistant, a report of a trial[1] at Southampton suggests that resistance is variable; soil and climatic conditions playing important parts. Elimination was secured by one application in this instance.

A prerequisite to successful treatment is a maximum leaf surface induced by applying sulphate of ammonia ($\frac{1}{2}$ oz. per square yard) or nitrate of soda at the same rate, making the application about a week before treating with Methoxone (M.C.P.A.) or 2-4-D (D.C.P.A.). Fertilizer dressing at the same time as treating tends to be less beneficial. It is not advisable to dress with quick-acting nitrogenous fertilizers late in the season in view of the danger of encouraging fungal diseases. Excellent results have followed treatment as early in the season as March and as late as November, but it will be appreciated that climatic conditions play an important part.

Light rain does not lead to a reduction in their efficiency but prolonged torrential rain can nullify the effects.

Soil temperature is important and it will be found that heavy clay soils are less rapid in working up in the spring than light sands. Soil temperatures of 60–70 degrees are regarded as being very suitable, for they accelerate the action of the selective weed-killer. It is not advisable to apply during cold weather, but conversely during periods of hot, prolonged dry weather the weeds are less susceptible particularly on light sandy soils where they become tough and leathery. Gardeners should bear in mind the possibility of damage to ornamental plants, and care must be taken when spraying or dusting to avoid the fluid or dust coming into contact with these plants. Likewi e, damage can result from the use for mulching of mowings from lawns treated with these weed-killers.

It will be found in practice that there are differences in the reaction of various weeds to Methoxone and 2 4-D. The former may be more successful with many weeds, while others succumb more readily when treated with 2-4-D.

[1] Reed, F. J.: *Parks, Golf Courses and Sports Grounds; The Problem of Pearlwort.*

Chapter Eleven

Pests and Vermin

ᗡᗡᗡᗡ ∘ ᘓᘓᘓᘓ

LEATHER-JACKETS

Some years ago leather-jackets achieved the somewhat doubtful distinction of almost 'stopping the show', particularly as 'the show' was one of our famous cricket grounds. This pest played havoc with the turf, rendering good-class cricket on what was regarded as one of the best wickets, a thing of the past. Bare patches appeared upon this famous ground and spread with alarming rapidity. Eventually the situation was restored, and leather-jackets faded from the limelight, yet during their reign of terror, they were front-page sports news; no small achievement for an insect.

LIFE HISTORY. The larvæ or immature insects of daddy-long-legs or crane flies, are variously known as leather-jackets or tory worms. Many species of *Tipula* and *Pales* are pests of lawn turf.

There are four stages through which the insect passes during its life: (1) Egg; (2) Larva or leather-jacket; (3) Pupa (the resting stage); (4) Adult fly.

The long-legged, cumbersome-looking adult flies usually appear at about the end of June, increasing in numbers until early in September and disappearing during October. The male is much smaller than the female, and his body ends in a club, while the end of the body of the female is pointed. After mating the female lays her eggs, piercing the soil, the brief span of her life is a matter of a few days only; it is, however, estimated that during this time she lays no fewer than 400 eggs and laying continues from June until about the end of September. Hatching takes place in about a fortnight, and the small legless and frail-looking maggots feed upon humus in the soil. The larval stage lasts about nine months, the insect gaining in strength and resistance, and seeking new forms of diet. It is at this period that damaging effects on lawns are noticed, for the leather-jackets, living not deeper than about two inches in the soil, commence to feed upon the roots of lawn grasses. During periods of frosty weather they burrow deeper in the soil and their rough skins appear to enable them to withstand being frozen. When the weather is mild and the soil damp, the grubs may be seen moving over the surface and they even migrate from one lawn to another. When fully grown, they are about $1\frac{1}{2}$ in. in length, legless and dun-coloured. The skin which encloses the soft body is very leathery and the head is also hard.

It now turns into a pupa, and nests just below the surface for a period of from nine to fourteen days, and then works its body through the soil until about one-third emerges. The crane fly then makes its appearance, leaving the empty pupa case either projecting from, or on the surface of the soil. There is, fortunately, only one generation of these insects each year.

DAMAGE TO THE TURF. The grubs feeding upon and cutting the roots of the grasses cause thin or bare patches, playing havoc with golf courses, bowling greens, tennis courts or cricket grounds and playing-fields. Leather-jacket damage must not be confused with an attack by one of the fungoid diseases and can be distinguished, for when attacked by *Fusarium nivale* (Fusarium patch) or *Corticum fuciforme* (Autumn rust) the plants still preserve a strong undamaged root system. A superficial examination will not, however, indicate the insect responsible, particularly between February and May (the most troublesome time) and the turf should be lifted; for it may be found that wireworms (*Elater* spp.) are responsible. The latter is, however, recognizable by its hard yellowish body and its six legs. Chafer grubs can also cause similar damage, but those in no way resemble leather-jackets for they also have six legs and their bodies are 'dirty white' or creamy coloured.

DESTRUCTION. The maintenance of a healthy sward is of paramount importance and during an attack the turf should be dressed with nitrate of soda at the rate of $1\frac{1}{2}$ to 2 cwt. per acre.

The value of D.D.T. cannot be over-emphasized. As soon as damage is noticed dust with 5 per cent D.D.T. dust at the rate of $\frac{1}{2}$ oz. per square yard, or spray using 2 lb. D.D.T. paste in 400 gallons of water. This is sufficient for 800 square yards. The gamma insomer of benzene hexachloride 'Gammexane' gives excellent results. Applications of a $3\frac{1}{2}$ per cent dust, at the rate of 1 oz. per square yard, are recommended.

The 'St. Ives Leather-Jacket Exterminator' is also a most effective insecticide. After years of painstaking research at the St. Ives Research Station, this exterminator was discovered, and has been found very successful. It is made by mixing 16 parts by volume of Orthodichlorobenzene, 4 parts by volume of 10 per cent sodium oleate solution and 4 parts by volume Jeyes' Fluid. The ingredients are stirred together until the mixture reaches the consistency of blancmange and when this stage is reached a further 1 part by volume of Jeyes' Fluid is added. The emulsion is now diluted in the proportion of 1 gallon in 400 gallons of water and the application should be made at the rate of 1 gallon to the square yard. The grubs are brought to the surface and can be swept up and removed.

Crude or semi-refined naphthalene is often used on agricultural land and may be applied to infested turf at the rate of 2 to 3 cwt. per acre and watered in.

The following mixture is also recommended:

> 1 lb. paris green,
> 30 lb. bran,
> 1 pt. treacle,
> 2 gal. water.

Sufficient to treat 1 acre.

Paris green is a poisonous material and care must be taken in handling it. Gloves should be worn when mixing; the use of a stick for stirring is advised. On no account should this bait be applied to turf where cattle are fed.

The proprietary leather-jacket destroyers offered by seedsmen and sundriesmen are also effective, and should be used in accordance with the manufacturers' directions.

Application of lead arsenate powder at the rate of $\frac{1}{2}$ oz. per square yard has been found beneficial; but if it is desired to combine leather-jacket and worm destruction in one operation the rate of application should be increased to $1\frac{1}{2}$ oz. to the square yard.

WIREWORMS

Grassland and sports turf provide conditions favourable for the development of this insect, and it has been estimated that the population of larvæ exceeds 1,000,000 per acre. Several species which are larvæ of click beetles or slipjacks (*Elater* spp.) are responsible for damage to lawn turf.

LIFE HISTORY. The four stages of life are: (1) Egg; (2) Larva or wireworm; (3) Pupa; (4) Beetle.

The click beetle is an insect which appears to land upon its back on an astonishing number of occasions and springs into the air with a sharp click, hoping, no doubt, to fall upon its feet.

Click beetles are dark brown in colour with wings covered by hard wing cases. They vary in size from $\frac{1}{4}$ to $\frac{1}{2}$ inch long and during the winter months they shelter above ground level, seeking protection under dead leaves, clods of earth or stones. The life of an adult insect is about one year. Emerging about the middle of May, they can be seen on plants until the end of August. Their food is foliage and flowers; the female lays her eggs during June and July, burrowing into the soil and laying them singly or in clusters. The eggs are round, white and small. The larval stage lasts from four to five years and the pupal stage about three weeks. When first hatched they are semi-transparent and look fragile, but gain in strength and become darker in colour as they grow older. Their colouring varies but the species usually found in turf are a pale yellow and vary in length from $\frac{1}{2}$ to $1\frac{1}{2}$ in. The body of the insect is hard and cylindrical, with three pairs of legs near the head. Wireworms are often confused with millipedes, but as their name suggests, the latter have many more pairs of legs along the whole length of their bodies.

DAMAGE TO TURF. The roots and lower parts of the grasses are eaten and small scattered, disfigured patches may be observed during April and May. The turf must be lifted to discover whether wireworms leather-jackets, or chafer grubs are responsible. On newly made lawns' wireworms are most likely to cause damage for two or three years,' particularly on light sandy soils.

DESTRUCTION. When preparing the soil before sowing seeds or laying turf a sharp look-out should be kept for pests of all kinds, and if wireworms are found when digging is in progress, as many as possible should be killed. Fallowing is advised where the pest is known to be troublesome. The application of crude naphthalene at the rate of 3 oz. to the square yard is also recommended if wireworms are noticed or suspected, and this should be forked into the soil. The production and maintenance of healthy turf will reduce the chances of destructive attacks.

It is suggested that 'Gammexane' applied as recommended for leather-jackets may prove effective.

Birds and many insects eat wireworms but a disadvantage is that they are likely to tear lawns and greens in an effort to locate the grubs. Moisture appears to be essential to the life of the insects, and they are easily killed in the egg, young larval and pupal stages by continued dry weather.

At the onset of an attack the turf should be rolled and a dressing of sulphate of ammonia applied at the rate of $\frac{1}{2}$ oz. per square yard, the fertilizer being mixed with sand or sterilized soil in the proportion of 1 part fertilizer to 4 parts sand or sterilized soil.

Kainit at the rate of 2 oz. to the square yard is also recommended, mixed with sand or sterilized soil in the same proportions.

FEVER FLY

When discussing leather-jackets and wireworms, lifting damaged turf to discover the insect or insects responsible was recommended. During such an examination, small greyish-brown grubs, superficially not unlike small leather-jackets, may be discovered and may be larvæ of the fever fly (*Dilophus febrilis*).

LIFE HISTORY. (1) Egg; (2) Larva; (3) Pupa; (4) Adult fly.

The fever fly[1] is small and black and the female has a circle of spines on her front pair of legs, which are used when pushing aside soil or manure to form a burrow in which to lay her eggs, the exact number of which is not known; but it is thought to be several hundreds. Egg laying takes place in May.

The larvæ when newly hatched are small, colourless and transparent, with the legless body divided into twelve segments, the last one bearing a pair of spiricles or breathing tubes.

The grub grows rapidly and, in fact, outgrows its skin which it casts off, a new one having formed beneath. This process takes place three times, and when in the fourth stage, the grub is said to be fully grown.

The pupal stage is next reached and lasts for about a month. It is possible to recognize the male from the female in this stage, as the former has larger eyes and three pointed processes on the top of the head, while the female has minute eyes and only one process.

The adult flies emerge late in September, mate, and the female lays eggs which give rise to progeny to overwinter in the grub stage.

There are two generations a year.

DAMAGE TO THE TURF. Fortunately the grubs of the fever fly do not feed exclusively upon the roots of the grasses but eat also decaying matter in the soil. The female fly has a preference for laying her eggs in dung heaps, and the application of farmyard manure may attract the fly to lawns and greens or the eggs or larvæ may be introduced with the manure.

Damage is not so serious as that caused by leather-jackets or wireworms and usually consists of small thin patches where groups of insects are feeding. Birds, however, may increase the damage by tearing lawns and greens when in search of the grubs. Fever fly grubs can be mistaken for small leather-jackets but they are easily distinguished by their well-developed shining brown heads.

DESTRUCTION. Applications of lead arsenate powder at the rate of 2 oz. to the square yard are suggested, but D.D.T. and 'Gammexane' have given promising results in preliminary trials.

[1] Morris, H. (1922): Bull. Ent. Research XIII.

CHAFER GRUBS

Larvæ of the June bug (*Phyllopertha horticola*) are often troublesome in lawns and sports grounds, eating the roots of the grasses.

LIFE HISTORY. (1) Egg; (2) Larva or chafer grub; (3) pupa; (4) June bug or cockchafer.

The June bug or cockchafer measures about an inch in length; has a black body covered with grey down and its wings are covered by hard reddish-brown wing cases. The female lays her eggs in the soil and the larvæ hatch out during the summer months. They remain in this stage for three years and they then pupate at a depth of two feet.

DAMAGE TO THE TURF. When the soil is not prepared thoroughly prior to sowing, newly sown turf is attacked. The grubs are, however, troublesome in all types of grassland and they disfigure the turf in a similar way to leather-jackets and wireworms.

To identify with certainty, it is necessary to lift the turf where it is attacked, and then to search for the insect responsible.

DESTRUCTION. In recent trials D.D.T. as advised for leather-jackets has proved effective. On small lawns stripping the affected parts, hand-picking and destroying the grubs is recommended but this is generally a very laborious means of eradication.

An application of naphthalene at the rate of 1 oz. to the square yard could also be made and then watered in.

In America, lead arsenate has given good results and when the grubs are near the surface, normally during September, it is well worth a trial. One ounce of lead arsenate should be allowed for one square yard. Heavy rolling during October with the object of crushing the grubs is also suggested.

DUNG BEETLE GRUBS (*Aphodius* sp.)

These are smaller than chafer grubs but rather like them. They are often found in the turf during the spring and while they cause little harm themselves, birds searching for them prove very destructive. Lead arsenate at the rate of 1 oz. to the square yard is recommended as a control. D.D.T. is also worthy of a trial.

ANTS

DAMAGE TO THE TURF. When a colony is formed under a lawn or green, an uneven surface is often produced and damage may be caused to the roots of the grasses.

DESTRUCTION. Many excellent proprietary ant-killers are available and those containing 'Gammexane' give particularly good results if used in accordance with the directions given by the manufacturers. Carbon disulphide, a highly inflammable liquid which liberates a poisonous gas, can be poured into the burrow by means of an oil-can and the hole should then be sealed. Care should be taken not to spill the liquid on to the turf, and the person making the application is advised not to smoke. Some local damage to the grasses around the mouth of the burrow or nest may be noticed. Calcium cyanide (Cyano-gas) used extensively for fumigating greenhouses has possibilities as an ant-destroyer. A pinch should be added to the soil at the mouth of the burrow. Handle this with care, and apply very sparingly or damage to the sward will result.

MINING BEE (*Andrena armata*, Emelin, and *Andrena fulva*, Shrank)

This bee burrows into the soil but causes little damage; it can be destroyed by applications of carbon disulphide and calcium cyanide, applied as recommended for ant-destruction.

RABBITS

Reports published in New Zealand[1] reveal that a pair of rabbits can produce six litters per year, and if the average number of offspring is six per litter, it will be appreciated that without control the rabbit pest may become serious in a short time. Grassland with a high rabbit population is likely to deteriorate and on golf courses and sports grounds where high-quality turf is required, steps must be taken to destroy the animals and to prevent further invasion.

METHODS OF DESTRUCTION. The steel trap or gin is inhumane and comparatively ineffective, and its use should be forbidden by law. The most humane and effective method of destroying rabbits is by fumigation, gas or dust being pumped into the 'runs'. There are many good proprietary exterminators which can be obtained through seedsmen and sundriesmen who will gladly furnish details on request.

A hose fixed to the exhaust pipe of a car or motor-cycle will bring about carbon monoxide poisoning and is very effective. The hose should be led down the burrow and the engine run gently for a quarter of an hour. The gas, which is heavier than air, flows into the lower burrows, reducing loss by leakage.

When a golf course or sports ground has been cleared of rabbits, special rabbit-proof fencing should be erected.

[1] Munrow, D., and Wright, R. (1933): *The Rabbit Pest and its Control*. New Zealand Department of Agriculture Bulletin 157.

MOLES

A considerable amount of damage is caused to grassland, golf courses and sports grounds by moles.

METHODS OF DESTRUCTION. Poison baits are usually relied upon, Nux vomica, Paris green, London purple, and phosphorus paste being the most widely used. Baits containing 10 per cent of either powder or liquid red squill are also effective. Worms dipped in strychnine were once almost a standard remedy, but the sale of strychnine, except for medicinal purposes, is now forbidden.

It has been found that two or three castor oil beans placed in the run will rid the ground of moles but these beans, in common with other baits, are poisonous to animals and therefore must be used with care. Another method is gassing as recommended for rabbits; using such materials as Cymag and Cyanogas. Where moles are particularly trouble-some it will be advisable to call upon the services of a mole catcher whose address is obtainable from the local branch of the Agricultural Executive Committee.

Chapter Twelve

Fungoid Diseases

⤜⤜⤜⤜ ◦ ⤛⤛⤛⤛

The intensive cultivation of any plant is likely to be followed by fungoid diseases and the fine grasses are no exception. Reports indicate that turf diseases are more prevalent than they were twenty or thirty years ago, but it is not correct to say that diseases which now cause a great deal of trouble were unknown in earlier days. It is probably more accurate to say they were not noticed so frequently. Sulphate of ammonia is invaluable as a weed-destroyer, but its continued use in excessive quantities after weed-destruction has been accomplished should be discouraged, for it would appear that by forcing the turf, particularly in the late summer, a soft luscious type of growth is encouraged, and this is particularly susceptible to attack.

FUSARIUM PATCH

FUNGUS RESPONSIBLE. The organism responsible is *Fusarium nivale*,[1] a fungus which during the winter months exists as dark brown mycelium embedded in plant tissues. Moist conditions favour the spread of the disease and infection is first noticed in May and again during September and October; but when lawns are watered regularly, it can occur throughout the summer. At this time, however, the grasses are usually vigorous and not so susceptible. During mild winter weather, attacks are not infrequent.

SYMPTOMS. It is during the autumn months that the disease is likely to be noticed when the brown circular or irregularly shaped patches appear, and as spores are blown in the wind, it can spread quickly.

From the appearance of these discoloured patches on lawns and greens the disease gets its name, the patches varying in size from as small as a penny to larger areas a foot across, often joining one another to render unsightly large areas and destroying the grasses. If a piece of the infected turf is cut out and covered by a piece of glass placed over a box,

[1] Bennett, E. T.: *Fungus Diseases of Bowling and Golf Greens.* J. Agric. Educ. Association, p. 164 (1935).

132

9a.   Fusarium patch on sea-washed turf

9b.   Section of a Fairy Ring

10a. Dock one month after treatment with 2, 4-D (D.C.P.A.)

10b. Turf showing effects of selective weed-killer

the bottom of which has been removed, the cotton-like growth of the fungus will appear in a day or two.

PREVENTION AND CURE. To prevent attacks strong vigorous turf should be maintained and sulphate of ammonia should not be applied after the end of July.

The disease can be spread by spores being carried on footwear, and wherever possible, walking over lawns and greens should be avoided, particularly in the early stages of an attack.

Mercuric chloride and calomel have proved invaluable in the control of this disease: mix 1 oz. calomel and 1 oz. mercuric chloride with 20 lb. sand. This is sufficient to treat 50 square yards of turf.

Effective control is also obtained by the use of Malachite Green Bordeaux which can be purchased from most seedsmen, horticultural chemists and sundriesmen, or the ingredients can be obtained and mixed by the user as follows:

Solution 1. Dissolve a $\frac{1}{4}$ oz. of Malachite green powder in $\frac{1}{2}$ gallon of water, shaking for a few minutes.

Solution 2. Dissolve three level tablespoonfuls of copper sulphate (fine crystals) in 1 gallon of hot water, using a wooden tub.

Solution 3. Six heaped tablespoonfuls of hydrated lime should be put into a 2 gallon watering-can and water added slowly and stirred well. 'Sofnol' and 'Limax' are excellent proprietary brands of lime.

To prepare the final solution:

Pour Solution 3 into a knapsack sprayer, using a strainer, add Solution 2, stir for a minute, or shake the sprayer, then add Solution 1. This quantity of mixed fungicide will treat 150 square yards and applications will be found most effective during dull weather or in the evening. Bright sunlight should be avoided. Treat the whole lawn, not only the affected areas.

A knapsack sprayer is preferred to a watering-can, as a fine mist spray will be found the most satisfactory means of securing contact between the grasses and the fungicide. Treatment should be given weekly during March and April in the south, and during April and May in the north.

Autumn spraying is more important and should be repeated at weekly intervals in September and October.

Cutting should take place before spraying and not after, and frequent cutting is preferable to close infrequent mowing.

During an attack curtail watering as far as practicable and stimulate the grasses by dressing with sulphate of potash at the rate of 1 oz. to the square yard. Regular switching with a bamboo cane preferably during the early morning will disturb dew upon the leaf blades and tend to minimize or prevent attacks. Reseeding areas where the turf is weak or bare after the disease has been controlled, should take place as quickly as possible, or weeds will appear. Routine aeration of the soil is also advised. Treatment does not provide immunity from one season to another, and the fungicides should be applied as advised to prevent the reappearance of the disease on turf which has suffered from attacks in previous years.

AUTUMN RUST

FUNGUS RESPONSIBLE. *Corticium fuciforme*, formerly known as *Isaria fuciformis*, causes Autumn Rust, or as it is sometimes called, the 'Corticium disease'. Lawns upon all types of soil are likely to be attacked, but the disease is more prevalent in the southern counties, although it occurs in other parts of England and in Scotland.

SYMPTOMS. The first signs of an attack are observed when the leaf blades of the grasses assume a pinkish or yellow colour and later they may turn a reddish-brown, particularly if the weather is damp. If a piece of the infected turf is cut out and placed under glass as described for Fusarium Patch, the fungus will be detected. When a lawn which is suffering from an attack is examined closely, a gelatinous growth will be found between the plants where the turf is highly coloured by the disease.

The extent of the damage is governed to a large degree by the condition of the turf and the climatic conditions at the time of the attack. The fungus may persist for only a few days—merely damaging the tips of the leaves—or the attack can continue, forming brown or bleached patches, resembling Fusarium Patch and killing the grasses.

The disease organism remains in the turf and resumes activity when conditions are favourable. Attacks can therefore recur in succeeding years even though the lawn is treated with fungicide, and spraying as a preventive measure is therefore recommended.

PREVENTION AND CURE. The disease usually appears during September and early October, but when lawns are watered regularly earlier attacks can be expected, and they also continue later when the weather is mild.

Spraying with Malachite Green Bordeaux as advised for Fusarium Patch, or dressing with mercuric chloride and calomel, will be found effective. Lawns subject to attacks should receive treatment at the end of August, and during September and October at intervals of one week.

FUNGOID DISEASES

FAIRY RINGS

FUNGUS RESPONSIBLE. Several fungi are responsible for fairy rings, but one of the most common is *Marasmius oreades*.

SYMPTOMS. A fairy ring consists of three zones with the grasses growing luxuriantly and dark green in colour on the outer and inner bands, while the central zone appears to be dead and dying.

When the spores of the fungus commence to grow, the hyphæ or cotton-like threads explore the soil, breaking up and rendering available ammoniacal and organic nitrogen compounds, inducing a dark green luxuriant growth. After a while the grasses appear to suffer from such over-feeding or are parasitized by the fungus growing outwards is then stimulating the plants in the outside zone. As the hyphæ die out in the inner band, recolonization by grasses takes place and these living in soil enriched by the fungus are deep in colour and so form the inner zone.

Turf on light sandy soils is most liable to attack from this disfiguring disease.

PREVENTION AND CURE. When the soil is fed well attacks are not common. Acid conditions are also likely to favour the development of the fungus.

(a) Malachite Green Bordeaux: spray infected areas as described for Fusarium Patch. (b) Formalin: add $\frac{1}{2}$ lb. for 20 gallons of water, and spray or water on to the turf. (c) Iron Sulphate: add 1 lb. to 4 gallons of water, and apply by means of a watering-can, using $\frac{1}{2}$ gallon of the fungicide to each square yard. Treatment with any of these preparations should be repeated at least once a fortnight and prior to spraying or watering, the soil should be pierced with a 'Sisis' solid-pronged fork to aid absorption.

DOLLAR SPOT

Sclerotinia homœocarpa, formerly known as *Rhizoctonia*, is the causal organism of the disease which, although common on turf in America, it is not met with frequently in Britain.

SYMPTOMS. Circular spots from 1 to 3 inches in diameter, sometimes running together to form irregular patches, appear upon lawns at any season of the year, but are more likely during mild, wet periods in the early autumn.

PREVENTION AND CURE. Abundant moisture and high acidity are conditions favouring the disease.

Copper and sulphur fungicides prove ineffective. In America[1] calomel

[1] Rhode Island Agr. Expt. Station Bull. 245.

is used mixed with dry sand as a carrier. Three ounces of calomel with 30 to 40 lb. of sand are allowed for 1,000 square feet of turf.

SHAGGY CAPS

FUNGUS RESPONSIBLE. *Coprinus comatus*, which grows freely on made-up land or tippings.

SYMPTOMS. The familiar shaggy caps decompose into a black objectionable mass.

PREVENTION AND CURE. No control is known but treatment with 'Sterizal' powder soil sterilizer is worthy of a trial.

Fungoid Diseases of Seedling Turf

Newly sown swards often exhibit symptoms of disease. The fungi most likely to cause trouble are:

1. *Pythium de Bar anum*, responsible for 'damping off'.

2. *Olpidium* spp., found in the roots of seedling *Agrostis*.

3. *Cladochytrium cæspitis*, a parasitic fungus which attacks many species of grasses.

SYMPTOMS. As the fungal organisms spread through the tissues of the grasses, the plants are enfeebled and assume a reddish hue.

PREVENTION AND CURE. Spraying with Cheshunt Compound is suggested.

Non-Fungoid Growths

LICHEN (*Peltigera canina*, Linn.)

SYMPTOMS. On acid soils or on neglected lawns the overlapping brown leaf-like structures appear.

PREVENTION AND CURE. Soil in good fertility and well-managed lawn turf is not likely to be invaded.

When this lichen appears, liming and later applications of general fertilizers are recommended.

ALGA (*Nostoc* sp.)

SYMPTOMS. This blue-green alga occurs on water-retentive soils.

PREVENTION AND CURE. A capped or hidebound surface, particularly on heavy soils, is more likely to show signs of this alga. Good management with soil aeration is essential. Watering with a dilute solution of sulphate of iron is suggested.

136

Chapter Thirteen

Manures and Manuring

❧❧❧❧ ⦿ ❦❦❦❦

FERTILIZERS FOR LAWNS AND SPORTS GROUNDS

Mention has been made of the marked differences which exist in the production of fine turf for lawns as compared with the cultivation of agricultural pastures, differences so great that greenkeeping and grass-land management are poles apart. This must always be borne in mind for in recommending fertilizers and manurial programmes, principles will be advocated that are contrary to good farming practice. But the farmer seeks to produce bulk, we require good quality dwarf turf, and naturally our methods must differ.

The Acidity Theory

A great deal of controversy followed the publication, in 1925, of the results of experiments conducted in the United States of America by the United States Department of Agriculture in conjunction with the United States Golf Association. This report showed that weed-free plots of Rhode Island Bent (*Agrostis tenuis*, Sibth) treated with monthly applications of sulphate of ammonia or ammonium phosphate were less prone to weed invasion and more free from worms than plots dressed with nitrate of soda or lime. The soil of the various test plots was also found to be more acid where sulphate of ammonia or am-monium phosphate was used and the conclusion was drawn that weed invasion was less likely in turf of this kind by the application of fer-tilizers with an acid-reaction.[1] The publication of a booklet increased interest in this country, but unfortunately later statements encouraged the belief that weeds would be automatically destroyed by induced acidity, claims which were never made by the Americans whose experi-ments were conducted upon plots which were free from weeds and not upon turf containing a weed population.

[1] Hackett, N.: *Soil Acidity, the Vital Importance of Top-dressing and Other Notes.*

Undoubtedly species of *Agrostis* and *Festuca* can withstand a degree of acidity unsuitable for the growth and development of many of the broad-leaved weeds, but the effects of sulphate of ammonia are as yet not completely understood and the question we must ask ourselves is: 'How does sulphate of ammonia effect the eradication of weeds?' One is inclined to subscribe to the view that the inducement of more acidity or less alkalinity is only part of the story and probably not the most important. Most weeds are low in carbohydrates and sulphate of ammonia has a toxic action upon them. A further aspect and probably the most important is its selective corrosive action.

Most weeds are broad-leaved and when dressed with sulphate of ammonia and sulphate of iron in the form of lawn sand a greater proportion of the dressing remains upon them. The effects of the application are not so pronounced if followed by rain, as when sunshine follows the dressing.

The establishment of acid conditions by the excessive use of sulphate of ammonia is undesirable, but for weed inhibition and elimination it is valuable, particularly in association with sulphate of iron as ingredients of lawn sand.

Nitrogenous Manures

Nitrogenous manures promote vigorous growth and in farm and garden practice they are usually employed to give vitality and an increase of foliage.

As a general rule excessive nitrogen is not advantageous for lawn grasses, as soft growth results and the turf becomes susceptible to fungoid diseases.

Used with discretion, bearing in mind that the fine grasses can withstand a degree of acidity, they are among the most useful fertilizing agents.

SULPHATE OF AMMONIA

When discussing the so-called 'Acidity Theory' prominence was given to this valuable aid to the maintenance of fine turf. It is a white crystalline odourless salt completely and readily soluble in water. In its manufacture volatile ammonia gas is neutralized with sulphuric acid and the change brought about is expressed as follows:

$$2\,NH_2 \quad + \quad H_2SO_4 \quad = \quad (NH_4)_2\,SO_4$$

| Ammonia | Sulphuric acid | Sulphate of Ammonia |

The value of this fertilizer has already been noted as an ingredient with sulphate of iron in lawn sand. Here its selective corrosive action destroys the weeds.

Under this heading we will first of all consider sulphate of ammonia purely as a fertilizer.

Doubt exists as to the actual form in which the grasses take up nitrogen from the soil and while the normal food of plants appears to be nitrates, it is also contended that many plants rich in carbohydrates assimilate ammonia nitrogen easily, whereas those low in carbohydrates may suffer from ammonia injury where the concentration is too high. If this theory is correct it would explain the superiority of sulphate of ammonia when used judiciously but it should not be regarded solely as a fertilizer to induce acidity. A slightly acid condition in the surface soil is probably advantageous and can be obtained by dressing with peat, sand and compost, and not by means of fertilizers.

How AND WHEN TO APPLY. 1. As a fertilizer, sulphate of ammonia should be applied at the rate of $\frac{1}{2}$ oz. to the square yard and watered in, or previously mixing the fertilizer with five times its weight of compost or sterilized soil. On no account should it be used except when mixed with compost or watered into the sward.

2. As a spring dressing for lawn turf it will prove valuable.

3. As a weed eradicator, in the form of lawn sand prepared as follows:

   (a) 3 parts sulphate of ammonia; 1 part sulphate of iron (calcined); 20 parts sand.

The mixture can be broadcast at the rate of 4 oz. per square yard.

   (b) 35 parts sulphate of ammonia; 15 parts sulphate of iron (calcined); 50 parts sand.

This should be used for 'spot' treatment of individual weeds.

For spot treatment of weeds, sulphate of ammonia can be applied to the individual weed by means of a special ejector. It should never be broadcast unless mixed with soil, peat, compost or other materials.

NITRO-CHALK

To counteract the effects of excessive acidity this is a most valuable fertilizer.

Ammonium nitrate is fused with calcium carbonate and the resulting fertilizer contains 15·5 per cent nitrogen, half of which is in the form of ammonia and the other half nitrate. Experiments indicate that worm and weed invasion may follow repeated applications but where turf is showing signs of excessive acidity applications are recommended.

How AND WHEN TO APPLY. For lawns and sports grounds on excessively acid soils this concentrated fertilizer presents great possibilities.

It can be used for spring or summer dressings at the rate of 1 oz. to 6 square yards, mixing the fertilizer with six times its own weight of top dressing mixture or sterilized soil.

NITRATE OF SODA OR CHILE SALTPETRE

This is a natural product imported from Chile and contains 15·6 per cent of nitrogen. Average samples are approximately 95 per cent pure.

Nitrate of soda is extremely soluble in water and very rapid in its action.

How and When to Apply. When lawns or sports grounds are suffering from attacks by insect pests and need a quick-acting stimulant, nitrate of soda at the rate of 1½ to 2 cwt. per acre is recommended. The fertilizer should be mixed with soil, sand or top dressing mixture, at the rate of one part fertilizer to six parts carrier prior to application.

Lawns to which nitrate of soda is applied appear to keep their colour throughout the autumn.

DRIED BLOOD

This is an organic manure, manufactured by drying slaughter-house blood by steam heat and then precipitating the nitrogenous material by adding ferric salts. It is dark, ruddy-brown powder and possesses a characteristic, rather offensive odour. It can be stored indefinitely without decomposing. Dried blood is usually regarded as comparatively slow acting but when applied to fine turf it appears almost as rapid as sulphate of ammonia and it is particularly valuable upon light soils as there is less danger of loss in wet weather. It does not induce acidity, and for this reason is used extensively upon bowling greens.

How and When to Apply. As a component of a fertilizing mixture or with sand or compost to act as a spreader.

SHODDY

This is the name given to the waste of woollen factories and is of very uncertain composition. The proportion of nitrogen varies from 4 to 12 per cent and the average is probably about 6 or 7 per cent.

How and When to Apply. Owing to its physical composition the use of shoddy is limited but could be incorporated with the lower spit when preparing land for sowing.

GROUND LEATHER

Leather is prepared from the hides of animals, which in the dry state contains about 16 per cent nitrogen. The hides are treated with tannin

11a.   Greater Plantain

11b.   Cranesbill

12a.   Silverweed

12b.   Self Heal

and impregnated with grease in order to preserve them, and this greatly reduces the manurial value.

Torrified leather is the name given to samples from which the fat has been extracted by the action of superheated steam. This contains a somewhat larger proportion of nitrogen and decomposes more rapidly.

Scrap leather is dried and ground, and contains about 5 per cent nitrogen.

HOW AND WHEN TO APPLY. Ground leather is often used as an ingredient of compound fertilizers, but is not recommended for direct use upon lawns and sports grounds.

HOOF AND HORN MEALS

These decompose very slowly and the proportion of nitrogen in commercial samples varies from about 7 to 15 per cent, with 12 per cent as a fair average.

HOW AND WHEN TO APPLY. For lawn turf they could be used as a source of slowly available nitrogen.

SLUDGE

Dried sludge results from the purification of sewage and contains about 2 per cent nitrogen.

HOW AND WHEN TO APPLY. Best used after composting.

SOOT

The condensed smoke of coal fires should not be confused with flue dust which contains potash. As a general rule soot weighs about 40 lb. per bushel and contains 2 per cent nitrogen, but as the bushel weight decreases the percentage of nitrogen becomes higher. Thus, samples weighing 28 lb. per bushel may contain 4 per cent nitrogen and those where the bushel weight is 15 lb., 7 per cent nitrogen. Apart from the chemical constituents the physical properties of soot must not be over-looked, for, as market gardeners realize, by applying to cold soils their temperature can be raised by its power of attracting the sun's rays. This is due to its dark colour. Soot is also a valuable insecticide.

HOW AND WHEN TO APPLY. An application at the end of March or early in April is recommended, using not more than one bushel to 400 square yards of established turf and mixing the soot with ten times its bulk of fine sterilized soil.

MALT CULMS

This is a by-product from the malting industries and consists of the rootlets of germinating barley. The nitrogen content is approximately 3·5 per cent.

HOW AND WHEN TO APPLY. Mix with good top-spit soil and allow to rot for at least a year.

Malt culms can also be supplied in a raw state at the rate of 1 oz. per square yard. Where worms are troublesome organic manures of this type must be used with great care. Heavy dressings are likely to conduce to worm invasion.

RAPE MEAL

Like malt culms this is a fertilizer of vegetable origin. Rape seed is used for the extraction of oil but the residue cannot be fed to animals as rape seed samples usually contain seeds of wild-mustard.

It has nitrogen content of about 5·5 per cent and on application decomposes rapidly.

HOW AND WHEN TO APPLY. As a spring dressing in a raw state at the rate of 1 oz. per square yard.

Frequent applications are discouraged as rape meal also tends to encourage worms.

Phosphatic Manures

The judicious use of phosphatic manures assists in the formation of a good root system and regulates the assimilation of nitrogen.

SUPERPHOSPHATE

Phosphoric acid is more readily available for plants than in any other phosphatic manure but for turf cultivation it must be borne in mind that its chief value is apparent on alkaline soils.

HOW AND WHEN TO APPLY. Where soil conditions are favourable as part of a balanced fertilizer or alone as a spring dressing at the rate of 1 oz. per square yard, mixing with four parts by weight of soil, sand or compost. For the pre-treatment of soil prior to sowing seeds.

BONE MEAL (Ground)

Bones from which the fat has been extracted under pressure, or by means of solvents in the manufacture of tallow, are ground and used for manuring. The extraction of the fat is an advantage for the fertilizer decomposes more readily in the soil, and is richer in phosphates and nitrogen. The normal content is approximately 20 per cent phosphoric acid and 4 per cent nitrogen and while described as a phosphatic manure, a more accurate description would be phospho-nitrogenous.

BONE MEAL (Steamed)

After the removal of fat, the bones are sometimes subjected to a further process of steaming in order to extract gelatine. The residue after steaming crumbles to a fine powder and is used as a manure under the name of Steamed Bone Meal. It is not so rich in nitrogen as ground bone meal, containing approximately 0·75 per cent nitrogen and 28 per cent phosphoric acid, but as a source of phosphoric acid it is superior.

BONE CHARCOAL, ANIMAL CHARCOAL OR SPENT BONE CHARCOAL

For sugar refining, bones heated in the absence of air are employed as a colour remover. After being used several times their effectiveness for this work is reduced and they are sold as a fertilizer. The content of phosphoric acid varies from 28 per cent to 35 per cent.

HOW AND WHEN TO APPLY. For the maintenance of bowling greens bone manures are used extensively, particularly in the form of bone meal.

They are also most useful as ingredients of compound fertilizers.

BASIC SLAG

This is a by-product from the manufacture of steel and a superior fertilizer was obtained when the Bessemer process of steel manufacture was employed. The modern 'open hearth' process does not produce such high-quality slag.

The crude product known as pig-iron is melted and air is blown through the molten mass in order to oxidize the carbon. The operation is performed in a specially constructed apparatus known as a 'converter' which is lined with lime which combines with the phosphoric acid present in the iron. Basic slag contains about 5 per cent phosphoric acid which is insoluble in water.

HOW AND WHEN TO APPLY. A disadvantage is that basic slag encourages the growth of wild white clover, but used in conjunction with nitrogenous fertilizers great improvement in the quality of lawn turf has been observed.

The popularity of basic slag for the improvement of agricultural pasture does not indicate that its use on lawn turf is automatic, in fact it is suggested that basic slag should not be applied to sports turf except as a result of expert advice.

Potassic Manures

Potassic fertilizers are not used extensively for lawns as they appear to increase the growth of clovers and other weeds belonging to the same natural order, but if nitrogenous manures continue to be used on a large scale, then to produce turf capable of withstanding fungoid attacks there must be an increase in the use of potassic fertilizers, especially on light soils.

SULPHATE OF POTASH

This occurs in natural deposits in France, Germany and the Dead Sea. Average samples are approximately 90 per cent pure. Sulphate of potash contains about 48 per cent potash, which is soluble in water.

How and When to Apply. This fertilizer is comparatively slow to act, but swards to which it is applied are much more green during the winter months.

Applications at the rate of ½ oz. per square yard are recommended, but normally potash is supplied as part of a general or balanced fertilizer dressing.

MURIATE OF POTASH

This occurs in natural deposits and like sulphate of potash is obtained from France and Germany. It is usually 80 per cent pure and contains 50 per cent potash.

How and When to Apply. In the same way as sulphate of potash.

FLUE DUST

German exports of potash have, during recent years, been interrupted by that nation's participation in martial activities which resulted also in an occupation of France. Flue dust proved an alternative source of supply. Collected from blast furnaces it contains potash in varying proportions from about 3 per cent to 7 per cent.

How and When to Apply. Can be applied alone at the rate of 1 oz. per square yard. For light soils the addition of compost is recommended.

General Manures

FARMYARD MANURE

The composition of farmyard manure is very variable but its value is undoubted.

The conversion of the 'fresh' manure into 'rotted' manure is termed 'malling', and unless farmyard manure is made properly it loses a great deal of its manurial value, losses which can be minimized with careful management.

Fresh manure should be spread to expose as large a surface as possible and it should then be drenched with cold water. If, after half an hour, it has not cooled, more water should be applied. A stack should now be made, beating and treading to make it firm during building.

A hole should be left at the top and if the temperature rises unduly, water can be applied. Very often the temperature rises far too high and the stack has to be re-made. Failure is usually due to loose stacking.

HOW AND WHEN TO APPLY. In the making of compost, farmyard manure, when and where available, is invaluable. Farmyard manure should be stored prior to using and sterilization is essential.

POULTRY MANURE

Kiln-dried poultry manure contains about 4 per cent nitrogen, 1 per cent phosphoric acid, 3 per cent potash, and 3·5 per cent lime.

If the raw material is used it will be appreciated that the chemical content will vary a great deal from the figures given.

HOW AND WHEN TO APPLY. Composting with fine soil or sand in the proportion of 1 part poultry manure to 20 parts soil or sand, and allowing to stand for six months is recommended. As a spring dressing 1 lb. can then be applied to 20 square yards.

FISH GUANO

This is not the excrement of fishes, but consists of dried fish offal. It is used frequently as an ingredient of mixed fertilizers.

BONFIRE ASH

The potash content is variable and is usually higher when twigs and branches are burned. Good ash is a valuable fertilizer, alkaline and slow acting.

HOW AND WHEN TO APPLY. Broadcast at the rate of 4 oz. to the square yard during late summer months.

PIGEON MANURE

Pigeon fanciers usually have plentiful supplies from their lofts and this is suitable for application to fine turf.

It normally contains about 2·5 per cent nitrogen, 1·8 per cent phosphoric acid, 2 per cent potash and 2 per cent calcium carbonate.

K   145

How and When to Apply. For spring and summer dressing at the rate of 1 to 2 oz. per square yard, mixing with four times its weight of soil or compost before making the application.

LIME

Much has been written, more will no doubt be said, concerning the use of lime upon fine turf. It is, therefore, appropriate to examine the position as it exists to-day and to endeavour to draw conclusions which will assist in this baffling but fascinating problem of turf management.

Lime is undoubtedly beneficial to the soil, liberating plant foods and stimulating the growth of plants, but on the other hand the close association of the grasses and the weeds makes the problems of greenkeeping difficult, for lime assists weed establishment.

It is much easier to induce alkalinity than acidity and alkaline soils are more likely to carry weed-infested swards than those which are slightly acid.

The excessive use of sulphate of ammonia will on the other hand lead to a deterioration in the ability of the soil to support a good grass population. Sulphate of ammonia renders the soil acid by the removal of lime and expressed in round figures for every hundredweight of sulphate of ammonia applied an equal weight of lime is removed. If the soil becomes too acid, the beneficial bacteria will be destroyed and fungoid diseases will have a much better chance of establishing themselves.

A Suggested Manurial Programme

A prerequisite to successful cultivation is a working knowledge of the chemical content and physical properties of the soil. Fertilizers for farm, garden, lawn or sports grounds must be applied to make good any deficiencies which exist and then to maintain the soil in such condition as is indicated by the plants which are to be grown.

On the chemical side we know that plants require nitrogen, phosphorus and potash but when cultivating fine turf we are faced with an additional problem, weed eradication. Farm and garden crops are normally planted to allow ease of access for weeding and if the fine grasses were grown as specimen plants or in neat rows, we should probably resort to entirely different methods from those which we now employ. Obviously the close association of grasses and weeds allows the undesirables to become established, as their removal by hoeing is not possible. We must, then, endeavour to produce fine dwarf turf, yet if we commit ourselves to an agricultural policy we shall not only stimulate the grasses but the weeds also. We have already noted that certain fertilizers promote the growth of clover, while sulphate of ammonia has a selective corrosive action and a toxic effect upon those plants which are low in carbohydrates.

The fine-leaved species of *Festuca* and *Agrostis* can withstand slight acidity whereas most weeds cannot thrive under similar conditions. Lime in excess is likely to lead to weed and worm invasion although lime is quite rightly rated highly by farmers and gardeners.

The hydrogenion concentration expressed upon what is known as the pH scale, represents the degrees of acidity or alkalinity of the soil and prior to embarking upon any manurial programme the soil should be tested. Fortunately a reliable soil testing outfit can be purchased for a few shillings and the results obtained will afford a practical guide to the degrees of acidity or alkalinity of particular soils.

The indicator changes colour as follows:

Red	at pH 3·0 changing to
Orange	at pH 5·5 changing to
Yellow	at pH 6·5 changing to
Greenish-yellow	at pH 7·0 to 7.5 changing to
Green	at pH 8·0 changing to
Blue	at pH 9·5

On the pH scale 7·0 indicates neutrality, values above 7·0 indicate alkalinity while values before 7·0 indicate acidity.

Those in charge of fine turf have, therefore, a ready means of testing soils.

NEWLY SOWN LAWNS

When a lawn is sown during the autumn it should be dressed in the spring with superphosphate at the rate of 1 oz. to the square yard, mixing the fertilizer with top dressing (1 oz. fertilizer to 8 oz. top dressing) and four dressings of sulphate of ammonia should be made at intervals during the late spring and summer mixing with sand or top dressing, or broadcasting at the rate of ½ oz. to the square yard and watering in.

During the second season reduce the dressings of sulphate of ammonia to three and at the end of the season and early the following spring, test the soil to discover the pH value.

147

ESTABLISHED LAWNS

As a general rule balanced fertilizers should now be applied. Sulphate of ammonia has played its part in weed inhibition, to continue to use it would probably produce conditions unfavourable for the finest sward. If weeds appear they can be destroyed by using selective weed-killers. The application of balanced fertilizers containing nitrogen, phosphorus and potash will lead to the production of grasses less likely to be attacked successfully by fungoid diseases and during the third and subsequent years a programme, subject to modifications, should run on these lines.

Dress in the spring with superphosphate at the rate of 1 oz. per square yard with 4 oz. of compost as a spreader, followed by top dressing after an interval of a fortnight. One to two pounds of compost per square yard can be used as conditions demand.

At the end of May apply a general fertilizer mixed with compost, allowing 1 part fertilizer, 7 parts compost, and apply at the rate of 8 oz. per square yard. Repeat the application about the middle of July and dress again towards the end of August with compost at the rate of 1 to 2 lb. per square yard.

COMPOSTING

A good mixture is the following:

> 2 parts sifted soil (sterilized)
> 2 parts peat (granulated)
> 1 part sand (sharp)

Applications should be made during the spring and early autumn as already advised.

LIME

Soil tests may indicate that lime is required, but light dressings only should be given. Heavy applications are not recommended.

POTASSIUM PERMANGANATE

Potassium permanganate or permanganate of potash has already been mentioned as a worm-killer and its use in the destruction of moss has also been discussed.

A report published in 1938[1] advocates the use of this material and suggests that it proves effective for the following purposes:

[1] Greening, C. B. (1938): Journal R.H.S. LX 111, 12, p. 561.

1. The stimulation of the growth of grass.
2. The destruction of 'mat'.

Its use as a worm-killer should be more general for the treatment is simple and safe, but in the control of moss it has been found that the benefits are not lasting. This, however, should not deter those in charge of turf from using permanganate, for the experiments carried out at Wisley indicate that the material has manurial benefits, encouraging the more vigorous growth of dark green grass.

A heap of mixed garden refuse (1 cubic yard) was on the 23rd July soaked with 6 gallons of solution containing 3 oz. of permanganate. The heap was lightly covered with a fork and treated with 3 oz. of permanganate dissolved in 3 gallons of water. Two further treatments each of 2 gallons of solution containing 2 oz. of permanganate were given on the 26th August and the 1st September. Before each application the heap was turned. Decomposition set in rapidly during the middle of August and a month later the heap was ready for use.

A 'control' of the same size was treated with water in the same quantities on the same dates, but the heap treated with permanganate decomposed far more rapidly. From the greenkeeper's point of view, it is reasonable to suppose that if permanganate will decompose garden refuse, it will also break down organic matter used for top dressing and render plant foods available more quickly.

EFFECT OF POTASSIUM PERMANGANATE ON THE GROWTH OF GRASSES. It has been found that permanganate of potash confers greater manurial benefit on old swards where organic material is not lacking.

More vigorous dark green growth is reported within a week of the application being made.

It is recommended that the rate of application should be varied to suit different soils. On heavy soils $\frac{1}{4}$ oz. of permanganate dissolved in 2 gallons of water and applied to 3 square yards is frequently effective, but on lighter soils it may be necessary to use 1 oz. in 1 gallon of water for each square yard.

THE DESTRUCTION OF 'MAT' BY USE OF POTASSIUM PERMANGANATE. Top dressing fine turf is likely to lead to an accumulation of materials and as the production of fine dwarf turf calls for frequent composting, 'mat' formation is likely to present problems. Particularly where lime is withheld and bacterial activity curtailed. The elimination of a 'matted' surface by the use of strong solutions will result in clean, rejuvenated turf.

Chapter Fourteen

Top Dressing

＞＞＞＞ ● ＜＜＜＜

The excessive use of sulphate of ammonia or any other artificial fertilizer on established turf can lead to a marked deterioration in its quality. The late Sir Albert Howard discovered in India that crops grown by native farmers were singularly free from insect pests and fungal diseases. In the East, 'custom is king' and the practice of utilizing waste products—animal and vegetable—to maintain soil fertility was founded upon the simple rules of good husbandry.

The basis of plant nutrition was humus, which produced crops without artificial fertilizers and without resorting to spraying and dusting with chemicals.

The advocates of composting will probably at this juncture assume that the maintenance of lawns and sports greens is entering a new era, but caution is advised.

The fine lawn grasses are those which in nature are found on the less generous soils and in their native homes survive with the minimum of nutrition. When used for lawns, bowling or golf greens and other field games it is necessary to replace the loss of food caused by constant defoliation; accordingly, feeding should be more generous than that enjoyed by the grasses of the salt marsh or upland pasture, but not sufficiently bountiful to encourage agricultural grasses to thrive upon a sports green laid or sown with fine-bladed species.

The weed problem requires careful consideration, for while selective weed-killers will play an increasingly important role in weed-elimination and perhaps inhibition, the manurial programme of which top dressing is an integral part must—as far as fine turf is concerned—be designed to discourage weeds and, on sports greens, earthworms.

Weeds in farm and garden crops are dealt with by harrowing or hoeing, but in the lawn they present a problem less simple.

Humus, however, is necessary for the maintenance of lawn turf. It is invaluable physically, making light soils darker and warmer, and giving cohesion to the sandy soils, enabling them to withstand drought

150

more readily. There is no defined chemical compositions for humus is a mixture of plants and often animals in varying proportions and at different stages of decomposition. Artificial fertilizers do not supply humus which, in addition to its nutrient function of supplying nitrogen, phosphates, potash, and other plant foods, plays a balancing role and acts as a buffer where an excess of boron—a trace element—is present in the soil.

Present-day knowledge of trace elements such as boron, molybdenum, cobalt and iodine, and their effect upon the lawn grasses is slight, but it is known that while tomatoes like boron and cotton thrives in a concentration of 15 parts per million, such a concentration would have a damaging effect on grasses.

The effect of the important trace element molybdenum upon clover and 'Yorkshire Fog' is of interest, for they can absorb from four to ten times as much molybdenum as timothy and smooth-stalked meadow-grass.

We are perhaps too prone to dwell upon the 'magic three', nitrogen, phosphorus and potash, and to neglect these trace elements, but time may reveal their wider importance. The modern grower is amused by the old Chinese custom of collecting pebbles and putting them around the fields, but boron acts best in the presence of silica and Chinese civilization is very old.

Top dressing, then, plays a vital part in lawn turf maintenance through the power of the grasses to produce basal shoots and to tiller. The application of top dressings stimulates tillering and, what is also of great importance as far as sports greens are concerned, assists in the production and preservation of a true, even surface with the minimum of rolling.

MAKING A COMPOST HEAP

Material which has rotted for two or three years is the most suitable for top dressing lawn turf, as it is usual to build heaps of alternate layers of soil and animal manure shaped like potato caves but less sloping at the sides and with a broad top to carry off the rain.

Heaps should be sited in close proximity to sheds to allow screening to be carried out during wet weather and it will often be found convenient to build against a wall. Several heaps should be made to ensure a continuity of supply, and as one heap is used another should be made.

PREPARATION

After rotting for at least one year (two or three years are better) the material is ready. Grasses and weeds will have grown upon the top and sides of the heap, and should be skimmed off and discarded. The heap should now be cut from top to bottom with a spade, and broken up with a fork and sifted through a quarter-inch mesh. After sterilizing, the top dressing material is ready for use.

STERILIZING

Market growers and gardeners know the value of sterilized soil and sterilization is carried out by many different methods to meet particular needs. Small quantities are baked in containers, but for sports ground use where larger quantities have to be handled, special plant is installed by engineering specialists whose advice should be sought by groundsmen and green keepers.

RATE OF APPLICATION

Sand is often added to the mixture of soil and manure prior to sterilization, but its addition or omission will depend upon the nature of the soil to be dressed.

An uneven surface may need a dressing at the rate of 2 lb. per square yard, but normal spring and autumn dressings can be regarded as 1 lb. per square yard.

SUBSTITUTES FOR ORGANIC MANURE

The amateur gardener may not find it possible to obtain animal manure and alternative supplies of organic material may have to be found. Rape meal and sludge have already been mentioned but leaf mould, malt culms, and granulated peat are also used extensively.

A good top dressing can be made as follows:

> 2 parts medium loam (sterilized)
> 1 part sand (sharp)
> 2 parts peat (granulated)

BROADCASTING TOP DRESSINGS

Distribution can be effected by hand or by the use of a 'distributor'. It is of great importance that dressings should be worked into the turf by means of wooden rakes, 'straight edges', chain mats or drag-brooms.

SAND

A sample of sea sand may contain as much as 60 per cent of calcium carbonate and consequently will act in the same way as a dressing of lime. In the circumstances pit sand is usually preferred.

Using Sand. It may be added to the ingredients used for a top-dressing mixture or applied alone. It will be found beneficial in improving the mechanical condition of heavy soils, and improving the sward by the promotion of tillering. The sand should be passed through a fine sieve and is usually applied during the autumn, winter or early spring. One ton should be allowed for about 600 square yards. The turf should be spike-rolled prior to the application, the sand rubbed in with the back of a wooden rake or on more extensive areas harrowed in, and then spike-rolled again.

CHARCOAL

Wood and bone charcoal are employed as top dressings and while the reason for the improvement which follows applications is not understood, it would appear that acting as an absorbent, surface drainage is improved. A marked improvement in the colour of the grasses usually follows a dressing with charcoal.

Using Charcoal. When land is wet it is advisable to use charcoal graded $\frac{1}{2}$ in. to $\frac{1}{4}$ in. mesh, but for more consolidated turf $\frac{1}{8}$ in. to $\frac{1}{16}$ in. mesh is suitable. Dressings at the rate of 1 lb. per square yard can be regarded as a standard but the quality can be increased to $1\frac{1}{2}$ lb. per square yard or increased to 2 lb. per square yard as circumstances demand.

Applications are made normally during the autumn, winter or early spring. Working it into the turf by means of a harrow, drag-brush, coir or chain mat on the back of a wooden rake. Spike-rolling before and after the application is recommended.

BREEZE

Where large areas require treating and charcoal cannot be employed owing to its large comparative expense, breeze will be found a useful substitute although the view is held that ultimately it restricts root development. While breeze may be used on lawns and fairways, it is not recommended for top-dressing sports grounds where players are likely to fall and injuries may be caused.

Using Breeze. Breeze can be graded to almost any degree of fineness but for lawn turf maintenance, $\frac{1}{8}$ in. and $\frac{1}{4}$ in. mesh for wet soils and $\frac{1}{16}$ in. mesh for firmer swards is recommended.

Make an application in the autumn, winter, or early spring. Harrow the turf, broadcast the breeze, and then roll it in.

The rate of application should be about $\frac{1}{2}$ lb. per square yard.

Chapter Fifteen

Mowing, Rolling, Raking, Aerating
and Watering

Most garden lawns are mown as a routine operation, the grasses being cut to keep them tidy and to assist in the maintenance of a lawn which is good to look at and pleasant to walk upon. Sports turf is cut to meet the requirements of the particular game which is played upon it and consequently a bowling green is more closely mown than is the outfield of a cricket ground.

The objects of mowing are:

1. To assist in the formation of a dwarf sward.
2. To control and destroy weeds by constant defoliation.
3. To encourage the grasses to tiller.
4. To produce an even surface.

Cutting is essential for the production of fine turf. The good lawn can be said to have been born with the invention of the lawnmower for, while the scythe has obvious advantages, it has a number of disadvantages—not the least of which is the average individual's inability to use it.

Lawn turf is normally cut with a small hand-driven mower, a motor or electric mower, or gang mowers hauled by tractor. The latter are used extensively upon golf courses and sports grounds.

A lawn or sports ground which has been neglected looks deplorable with the grasses long and choked with weeds, but it is remarkable how rapid is the improvement brought about solely by cutting, for most of the common agricultural weeds cannot withstand constant defoliation and gradually disappear when the turf is mown closely.

When discussing lawn grasses it was observed, when describing the stems or 'culms', that buds are formed near the base of the first shoot from which shoots called 'tillers' are produced. The power to 'tiller' is of great importance in lawn grasses, which are mown frequently, for the plant spreads, clothes the ground and thickens the sward.

WHEN TO CUT

The actual times will depend upon the purposes for which the sward is used but, generally speaking, most turf, whether on lawns or sports grounds, is not mown sufficiently early in the spring.

It must be realized that grasses will grow throughout the year if conditions are favourable and therefore if the weather and the soil are suitable the grasses can, in most parts of the country, be 'topped' during late February or early March with the machine set high.

During March two cuts, or 'toppings' will be made, while in April the cut will gradually be lowered until the grasses are mown as closely as desired.

For garden lawns and putting greens it is preferable to cut three or four times a week, and it has been proved that the weight of the mowings removed from lawns and greens treated in this way is less than that removed from lawns and greens mown once a week.

Cutting should continue as long as weather and soil conditions allow.

THE GRASS BOX

It is preferable to remove the grass box when mowing early in the year for the mowings will protect the newly mown turf from spring frosts. During periods of dry weather, providing the lawn or green is free from annual meadow-grass (*Poa annua*) and Yorkshire fog (*Holcus lanatus*) is not troublesome, the box should also be removed. If mowing is carried out following the application of fertilizers or selective weed-killers, the cuttings should be allowed to lie upon the ground for, unless the turf has been watered or rain has followed the application, then the mowings are likely to carry a proportion of the fertilizer, but it must be borne in mind that grass cuttings from a sward treated with selective weed-killers can also damage garden plants if removed and used for mulching.

Mowers

The area to be cut and the purpose for which the turf is required govern to a large degree the choice of mower. The following are the main types:

1. Gang mowers.
2. Hand mowers.
3. Horse, pony and donkey mowers.
4. Motor mowers.
5. Electric mowers.

1. GANG MOWERS

These are used to cut large areas of turf on parks, golf courses and recreation grounds.

They are drawn by tractor, but most models can be supplied with shafts for horse-draught instead of the usual tractor drawbar. This most efficient method of ganging allows each unit to follow its own ground level. For mowing what is termed 'hummocky' ground a set of disc rollers can be fixed to the front of each unit which enables the machine to negotiate the 'hummocks' without cutting off the tops.

The introduction of the gang mower caused a revolution in the cutting of golf course fairways, for a triple mower consisting of three 30-in. cutting units has a cutting width of seven feet; while a quintuple mower with five 30-in. cutting units has a cutting width of 11 feet 6 inches; and the cutting width of a septuple mower—seven 30-in. cutting units— is sixteen feet. It will be appreciated how quickly large areas of turf can be cut regularly in this way, in fact, a septuple mower drawn by tractor can cut ten acres per hour.

2. HAND MOWERS

Many and varied are the types of hand mowers, many and varied their uses. The type and size of mower purchased will depend to a great degree upon the size of the lawn, or green.

Garden lawns do not usually require such close cutting as sports greens and a good guide is to allow a width of about a quarter of an inch between the base of the sole plate and a line drawn between the front and back roller of the mower.

For bowling greens a 14–18 in. machine is normally employed with an extra thin, often reversible, bottom blade. These machines, available in models with eight or ten blades, are specially designed to ensure an extremely fine finish and reduce 'ribbing' to a minimum.

Putting greens require cutting with high-speed machines fitted with eight or ten blades and the usual sizes are from 12 to 18 inch. Under 'Motor Mowers' a method of combining several hand mowers is described for it will be appreciated that the constant mowing necessary for the maintenance of a first-class putting surface renders the hand-cutting of eighteen greens a costly operation.

For garden lawns, tennis courts, and cricket squares, 12–18 in. machines with eight cutting blades are found satisfactory.

3. HORSE, PONY AND DONKEY MOWERS

With the introduction of the petrol engine, horse-drawn mowers lost a great deal of their popularity but a number are still in use, and models are available from manufacturers.

4. MOTOR MOWERS

The size and type of motor mower required will depend upon the purpose for which the sward is used, and its area. The following is a guide:

For 10 acres, or more	42 inch
For 6	36 inch
For 5	30 inch
For 4	24 inch
For 3	20 inch
For 2	16 inch
For 1	14 inch

For golf greens the labour required for cutting can be reduced by using a specially designed two-wheel tractor, drawing three adapted hand mowers. This is, in fact, a miniature gang outfit for golf greens.

5. ELECTRIC MOWERS

These have been designed for lawns and bowling greens. A 14-in. machine is recommended for garden lawns, and an 18-in. machine for bowling greens. Models are available which are completely electrically driven, while others are fitted with motors which drive the cutting cylinder only.

MAINTENANCE

Instructions for using and maintaining are usually supplied with the machine and the recommendations of the manufacturer should be studied and followed. When printed on one side of a sheet of paper they should be fixed to the wall of the toolshed for easy reference. A most important part of the tool kit for a motor mower is a spare plug of the same make and type as that fitted to a new machine. The plug should be changed frequently. This is very necessary with two-stroke engines and the old plug should be sand-blasted at a garage to be ready for use in an emergency.

Rolling and Rollers

Moderation should be the keynote of rolling operations. Turf rolled when it is wet tends to become consolidated or hidebound and under such conditions, aeration is suspended and the sward suffers.

Many games call for heavy rolling, cricket and tennis are examples, but the harmful effects of consolidation can be counteracted by providing aeration by means of piercing or pricking.

Rolling dry turf imparts a waving movement which is beneficial and when a level surface has been produced, light rolling and top dressing will usually maintain it.

It is important not to roll wormcasts into the turf to smother the grasses. These should be brushed off before rolling takes place.

Rollers, like mowers, are designed to meet a multitude of needs. They are probably best described under the following headings:

1. Gang rollers.
2. Hand rollers.
3. Horse and pony rollers.
4. Motor rollers.
5. Wooden rollers.

Spiked rollers are described under 'Aeration' and the rollers referred to here are those used to level the surface of lawns and sports grounds.

1. GANG ROLLERS

For large areas such as golf fairways and cricket grounds, the most popular type is a triple gang roller designed to roll both undulating or flat surfaces. A well-known triple gang roller has three units each 18 inches in diameter, consisting of double cylinder cast-iron rollers. The front roller is provided with a spring-loaded pull-bar to absorb shocks, and the units have central rear hitches so that they may be trailed in file for passing through narrow gateways. Ballast boxes can be supplied to fit to the frames of each unit in order that the weight may be varied as required.

Rollers of this type are usually drawn by tractor.

Another popular type particularly for undulating fairways, is a flexible gang roller which is available in two models, one with wooden rolls, the total weight of which is 15 cwt. and the other with cast-iron rolls and a total weight of 27 cwt. Its advantages are, that it distributes its weight evenly over the entire surface, it will not roll down all the high spots and leave the hollow unrolled, and in hollow ground the edges do not 'score' the grass.

2. HAND ROLLERS

Many types of hand rollers are in use to-day, special models being available for garden lawns, bowling greens, cricket pitches, etc. These are classified as 'Ordinary' or 'Water Ballast' roller and the particular type selected depends largely upon the requirements and preference of the purchaser.

For garden lawns 'Ordinary' and 'Water Ballast' rollers are used and a selection of the sizes and weights in common use is the following:

'Ordinary'

Width and diam. (inches)	Weight cwt. qr. lb.
14 by 14	1 3 0
16 by 14	2 0 0
18 by 16	2 3 0
20 by 18	3 0 14
22 by 20	4 0 0
24 by 22	4 3 0

Water Ballast (Double Cylinder)

Width and diam. (inches)	Weight empty cwt. qr. lb.	Weight full cwt. qr. lb.
20 by 20	3 3 7	4 2 7
22 by 22	4 2 0	5 3 21
24 by 24	5 1 0	7 1 7
27 by 27	8 0 14	11 1 0
30 by 30	10 1 14	14 3 0

Water Ballast (Single Cylinder)

Width and diam. (inches)	Weight empty cwt. qr. lb.	Weight full cwt. qr. lb.
21 by 21	3 3 14	5 2 0
24 by 24	4 2 0	7 0 0
27 by 27	6 3 0	10 0 0
30 by 30	9 0 0	14 0 0

For bowling greens specially designed rollers weighing from $4\frac{1}{2}$ cwt. to $4\frac{3}{4}$ cwt. are used, and these have a diameter of 33 inches and width of 33 inches. A similar type is suitable for hard tennis courts.

Rollers for cricket grounds are usually fitted with shafts for horse-draught, or interchangeable handrails. They are available in many sizes and weights, of which the following is a selection:

Standard Rollers in Two Parts

Width and diam. (inches)	Approx. weight cwt.	qr.
36 by 30	11	2
42 by 30	12	1
42 by 36	19	3
48 by 36	21	0
48 by 42	25	0

Water Ballast Rollers in Two Parts

Width and diam. (inches)	Approx. weight empty cwt.	qr.	Weight full cwt.	qr.
30 by 28	10	0	14	3
36 by 30	12	2	17	2
42 by 36	24	2	30	2
48 by 42	28	3	40	3

For level or undulating golf greens a Flexible Roller is highly recommended. It rolls the greens quickly, distributing its weight evenly over the whole surface and no cross rolling is required.

3. HORSE AND PONY ROLLERS

These are available in many sizes and weights and can be fitted with boxes for holding stones, gravel, and other material.

Width and diam. (inches)	Approx. weight cwt.	qr.
36 by 30	11	2
42 by 30	12	1
48 by 30	13	0
60 by 30	16	3
72 by 30	19	0

4. MOTOR ROLLERS

The weight and type of roller to be used will be governed by the condition of the soil and the purpose for which the turf is required.

AERATING AND WATERING

Models available range from a hand motor roller to a heavy diesel.

A hand motor-roller is particularly suitable for tennis courts, cricket outfields and football pitches where the soil or turf are too soft to allow heavier rolling.

A popular model is available in two weights and sizes.

Width and diam. (inches)	Weight cwt.
26 by 28	10
30 by 30	15

When supplied as water ballast rollers the weights for the sizes quoted are 13 cwt. and 20 cwt. respectively.

A light motor roller (petrol or diesel) intended for cricket, football and other sports grounds is manufactured and the following are the general sizes:

Working weight	If Ballast type
About 1½ tons	
About 2 tons	About 2¼ tons ballasted
About 2½ tons	About 2¾ tons ballasted
About 3 tons	About 3¼ tons ballasted

When a diesel engine is fitted these weights are increased by approximately 5 cwt. in each case.

A light motor roller is also available which will haul a triple mower, so that rolling and mowing can be carried out in one operation.

5. WOODEN ROLLERS

Wooden rollers impart a good finish to golf greens, bowling greens, and other fine turf and many types are manufactured.

HOLLOW WOOD ROLLERS. These are the lightest wood rollers made. They are built up of wood staves upon an iron frame, forming a hollow closed cylinder. They weigh only about two-fifths of the weight of a solid wood roller of the same size.

The sizes available include the following:

Water Ballast

Width	Diameter	Weight
3 feet	1 foot	100 lb.
4 feet	1 foot	130 lb.

Sand Ballast

Width	Diameter	Weight
3 feet	1 foot	90 lb.
4 feet	1 foot	100 lb.

SOLID ELM ROLLERS. These are usually made in sections 12 inches long and 12 inches in diameter; or 12 inches long and 9 inches in diameter; or in one piece 3 feet long. A popular model is in three sections, 12 inches by 12 inches, giving a total length of 3 feet and with a wrought-iron frame weighing 140 lb.

The 4 foot roller with a wood handle frame, and weighing 110 lb., is also used very extensively.

Raking

Their powers of renewal by the growth of basal buds enables lawn grasses to survive and indeed to colonize under conditions of close mowing.

Raking should not be relegated to its least important function the clearing of leaves and surface debris in late autumn or early winter, for routine raking and scarifying, the former with special wire rakes of the 'Springbok' type and the latter with scarifying machines, play a very important part in turf maintenance. Basal buds break more freely when the sward is raked regularly and raking and scarifying disturb the surface soil, which otherwise may become 'capped'.

Following applications of formulations for the destruction of weeds and moss, the rake or scarifying machine should be used for their removal.

Certain weeds, notably yarrow and clover are weakened when mown closely. Raking before mowing will bring them up so that they do not miss the blades of the mower.

Aeration

The importance of aerating the soil has been stressed throughout this work and the subject is returned to in order to introduce some of the implements and machines now available to assist greenkeepers and groundsmen in their tasks of maintaining fine turf.

Unfortunately, from the standpoint of turf maintenance, it is so often assumed that because a true level surface is required for a particular game, then that surface must be maintained by constant heavy rolling

162

The result is that the soil becomes consolidated, impervious to moisture, and incapable of supporting a first-class sward.

To offset these conditions and also to compensate for what is claimed in favour of the worm—that it aerates the soil—forking, spike-rolling, and the use of aerating machines must be resorted to.

HAND FORKS

These are made in two types: (a) with hollow prongs; (b) with solid prongs.

HOLLOW-PRONG PIERCING FORKS. The hollow-prong forks can be fitted with collecting troughs which enable the punchings to be emptied into a barrow instead of being discharged on to the ground and then collected. The prongs are tapered both internally and externally, making a slightly tapering hole which facilitates refilling with compost, and the internal taper permits the plug to pass right through the tube to the top.

The shape of the frame allows the operator to place his foot centrally, and thus give an even pressure and also there is no centre shaft to knock or rub his knee.

SOLID-PRONG PIERCING FORK. These are special forks with solid prongs, manufactured for turf-piercing or pricking. The most popular are fitted with strong handles which can undertake the additional strain of levering the turf when this is necessary.

TURF-PIERCING MACHINES

The introduction of the hollow-tine fork by William Paul of Paisley in 1919 was followed by many modifications and for larger areas the spiking or turf-piercing machine has been evolved.

Machines for spiking and hollow-tine forking are available which are hand operated, drawn by tractor or motor driven.

Spiking on the gang principle is usual on extensive areas of sports turf.

It will be appreciated that the design of machines of this type was not simple, for a forward movement is likely to result in the turf being torn unless the tines leave the soil vertically. To prevent tearing, tines are attached to swivelling bars, fixed to a weighted plate which is lifted and allowed to fall, or are made in the form of high-speed twisting drills which are driven into the soil.

THE SPIKED ROLLER

While the spiked roller does not pierce the turf as deeply as the deep turf-piercer, it has long been used by greenkeepers and groundsmen. A wooden spiked roller is used upon thousands of golf courses and sports grounds. The rollers are made in sections 12 inches long by 9 inches in diameter and each section is fitted with 65 spikes, so that a roller 3 feet long carries 195 spikes and covers three-quarters of a square yard with each revolution. A golf green 20 yards square receives no less than 104,000 punctures in one rolling, and a green or cricket table 40 yards square 416,000.

For golf fairways and other large areas tractor gang spiked rollers and spiked horse rollers are made.

SPIKED TURF-BEATERS

For aerating small areas the spiked turf-beater is invaluable. The heavy elm beater is fitted with a steel sole plate and carries galvanized steel spikes 2 inches long. It is lifted and beaten against the surface to force the steel spikes into the turf.

Water and Watering

The volume of water required by any lawn or green will depend upon the nature of the soil, and the purpose for which the turf is used.

Golf courses and recreation grounds suffer during drought years and the installation of a water supply is essential if first-quality turf is to be maintained.

WATER FROM STREAMS

Many clubs are fortunate in having streams running through their courses or grounds, and can utilize this source of supply.

TESTING SAMPLES

Prior to using water from any source, it is advisable to take samples each day for a week and to submit these for analysis. Sanction to draw from the stream should then be obtained from the appropriate authority.

PREPARATION OF A SCHEME

When it has been proved that the water is suitable and permission to use it granted, then a scheme can be drawn up by an expert. Probably means will have to be found to overcome irregularities in the flow of the stream and a catch pit, or sump, will have to be installed capable of holding an adequate reserve. The water will be pumped from the sump and carried through pipes and can then be distributed by sprinklers.

BOREHOLES

The cost of installing a water system where a borehole has to be sunk is relatively high, but water is essential for sports turf and in spite of the cost, where other methods are impracticable, must be resorted to.

Advice as to geology of the district must be sought and the work entrusted to experts. A borehole is taken out and often has to be sunk more than 400 feet deep before an adequate supply can be assured.

Various methods of raising water are employed and clubs must be guided by the expert in charge. The water can be pumped to a tank situated on the highest available point and fed to the greens, pitches or courts.

MAIN WATER

Where main water can be obtained it is much less expensive to instal, but it must be borne in mind that authorities are often very short of water at a time when it is most required by the greenkeeper and groundsman. Therefore, an independent supply is desirable if funds permit.

SPRINGS

Where springs yielding a constant supply exist it is usual to conduct the water to tanks and then to pump as required.

RESERVOIRS

Surplus rain water is often conserved in large capacity permanent reservoirs, but here again expert advice must be obtained before embarking upon the project.

WATERING LAWNS AND SPORTS TURF

The importance of water in the maintenance of fine turf is not fully realized until the onset of drought conditions, when golf courses, sports grounds, and lawns suffer alarmingly if inadequately supplied with water.

When describing the construction of a bowling green, it was mentioned that the foundation was so designed to provide quick drainage and it must therefore be borne in mind that such drainage is not only quick, but thorough. Accordingly, if a bowling green or for that matter, a lawn, golf green, cricket pitch or tennis court is allowed to become thoroughly dry it is most difficult to saturate it.

The application of water to turf is in most cases delayed until too late, and often applications are made to a 'hidebound' surface which is practically impervious.

To avoid this the weather must be watched carefully during the spring and sufficient water applied to keep the turf moist at all times.

Mole draining should not be undertaken if there is a doubt as to the suitability of the land and expert advice should always be sought.

How to Carry Out the Work. The most opportune times are in the late autumn or during the early spring, which are ideal for sports ground maintenance as surplus labour is normally available.

Wherever possible get on with the work in the late autumn for the turf is not likely to experience a period of dry weather following operations. There is a danger that spring drainage may be followed by hot dry weather which will crack the land and open up the coulter slits with a consequent choking of the mole drains.

This system derives its name from the tunnels which are made up by drawing a torpedo-shaped tube through the soil to a depth of from 12 to 18 inches. Greater care is necessary when draining sports turf than agricultural land and sports contractors are the best people to employ. There are many types of mole ploughs but for sports ground work a cleaner cut is made through the turf when the coulter has a disc knife in front of it and rollers are preferable to skids as they reduce damage.

The plough can be drawn by tractor or operated by cable haulage.

Drains are usually of $2\frac{1}{2}$- or 3-inch bore and when the work is in progress the men in charge must maintain constant supervision for if large stones are encountered a temporary halt must be called or the mole may be forced out of the ground. The ground must be studied carefully and the advice of the groundsman taken for he is likely to have a greater knowledge of peculiarities in contour.

Water should be allowed to travel with the fall of the ground and if a deep ditch is available it may not be necessary to put in a main pipe drain. The moles can be connected to the ditch by inserting pipes or even boiler tubes, the longer the better, in the moles. When a main drain is installed its level should be six inches below the moles, a most important point, for the average life of this type of drainage is perhaps three to five years and the moles can be cleaned in future years without disturbance to the mains. The distances apart at which the drains are drawn depends upon local conditions, three to ten yards being usual but on very wet land they are often much closer together.

To link up the moles with the main drain, dig to its depth and insert a length of 2- or 3-inch pipe drain into the moles. Refill the holes made with hard core; provide sufficient soil then return. Often the contours of the land encourage water to collect on the surface. 'Weep holes' should be installed by digging holes about 18 inches square and 3 inches deeper than the drains. These holes should be filled with hard core to within 4 inches of the surface, protecting the mouth of the hole with a piece of broken tile. Soil should then be used to complete filling and the turf replaced.

TILE OR PIPE DRAINAGE

Modern machinery enables a system of this kind to be installed with far less labour than was required twenty years ago and mechanical excavators will play an increasing part in sports ground construction. There are many which can be used in conjunction with a tractor, reducing labour costs to a minimum. Tile or pipe drains form the best and most permanent system but whereas mole drainage can be carried out upon an established sports ground with practically no serious curtailment of play, pipe drains should be installed when the ground is being made. Modern porous concrete pipes are gaining popularity and are highly recommended.

It should also be borne in mind that drainage for sports grounds and golf courses is a different proposition from farmland. The farmer wants to grow deep-rooting crops, whereas the greenkeeper and groundsman is more concerned with the provision of well-drained surface soil.

Pipe drains are normally laid on what is known as the 'herring bone' system, with 4- to 6-inch pipes for the main drains and 2- to 3-inch pipes for the spurs. The spurs are usually 20 to 50 feet apart as conditions demand.

As an alternative to the herring bone principle parallel lines of pipes are laid diagonally across the slope.

It is essential that a survey of the area be undertaken prior to installing costly drainage system and full use should be made of local knowledge such as the position of any minor springs. Always allow for a good fall and after the pipes have been laid test them thoroughly before filling the trenches with cinders to within 3 or 4 inches of the surface. Soil should form the remainder of the filling and finished off with turf.

LOCAL DRAINAGE

On small areas such as cricket squares, putting greens, tennis courts and garden lawns regular top-dressing with sand, charcoal or breeze reduces the necessity for pipe drains to a minimum. Often, however, waterlogging in certain localized parts of the sports field occurs. 'Weep holes' should then be constructed and even if there is no drainage system they will assist in removing surface water.

CONSERVATION

The disastrous effects of drought on many sports grounds could be minimized by conserving water. It will be found very beneficial to provide wells near to the outfall to retain water which would otherwise be allowed to run away. A reserve of this nature is seldom provided but its benefits are obvious.

DRAINING GARDEN LAWNS

The drainage of smaller areas of turf such as garden lawns sometimes presents difficulties and it is unwise to lay down rules. In very many cases pipe drainage is not required, for heavy retentive soils can be improved by introducing fine ash or sharp sand when preparing the seed bed. The manurial programme can also assist in improving the condition of the soil. Applications of sulphate of iron have a marked action in flocculating heavy clays and top dressing and forking can play their parts. The use of sulphur which coagulates the fine clay particles has proved very successful on many heavy clay soils, but results are not uniform. In the circumstances dressing a small area and recording results is advised. Applications at the rate of 1 to 4 oz. to the square yard of finely powdered sulphur are suggested. However, on badly drained, waterlogged soils it becomes necessary to install a drainage system and a 4-in. main, with 3-in. spurs set from 10 to 30 ft. apart as circumstances demand normally meets requirements.

Chapter Seventeen

The Lawn for Recreation

⋙⋙⋙ ◦ ⋘⋘⋘

A. Cricket

When early cricketers first made the summer air ring with the sound of bat on ball, they created not only a game but a tradition that has become part of the fabric of the English countryside, and nowhere are the strands woven more closely than in the village. Cricket has lost none of the charm which, for centuries, has made it the premier summer game, yet from time to time sports writers and others assert that mammoth scores on perfect wickets are detrimental. It is acknowledged that certain well-known wickets place the batsman in a dominating position, but it must be realized that if a wicket is to last for three days with the minimum of deterioration, then its preparation is likely to result in a surface which is near to perfection when the game commences.

It is as well to forget for a while the well-prepared county tables and to consider the village green and less prominent town club for here—alas—conditions are often far from good, and the batsman, instead of being on top, perchance takes his life in his hands when facing the fast bowler. An improvement in the wickets used for week-end cricket would result in a higher standard of play, for concrete practice wickets, while being valuable in giving young players confidence and allowing the development of good stroke play, are not fulfilling their purpose if bad match conditions are allowed to exist.

A New Ground

THE OUTFIELD

It is not essential that there should be a level surface, providing this is true and free from depressions. Drainage may be required and an adequate system must be installed where necessary. During the winter months hockey is often played upon the cricket outfield, and wear and tear can be heavy if hardwearing grasses do not predominate in the seeds mixture.

The following mixtures are suggested:

(a) For drier soils (smooth-stalked meadow-grass not available)

    50 per cent Perennial rye-grass (S.23)
    20 per cent Crested dogstail
    20 per cent Chewing's fescue
    10 per cent Brown top

(b) For drier soils (smooth-stalked meadow-grass available)

    50 per cent Perennial rye-grass (S.23)
    20 per cent Smooth-stalked meadow-grass
    10 per cent Crested dogstail
    10 per cent Chewing's fescue
    10 per cent Brown top

(c) For water-retentive soils

    60 per cent Perennial rye-grass (S.23)
    10 per cent Rough-stalked meadow-grass
    10 per cent Timothy (S.50)
    10 per cent Crested dogstail
    10 per cent Brown top

Six inches of top-spit soil should be available to form a seed bed after mechanical levelling has been carried out. The surface should be disced frequently, pre-treated with general fertilizer, and rolled to consolidate—care being taken to secure a fine tilth with a firm surface. Seeds should be surface sown by 'barrow' or 'fiddle', sowing and cross-sowing at a seeding rate of not less than 1½ cwt. per acre. Following sowing, the seed bed should be harrowed and rolled again.

THE WICKET

An area thirty yards square is normally sufficient to meet the needs of a club playing twice, or perhaps three times a week. Water-retentive soils will need pipe drainage and graded cinders should cover the pipes, care being taken to ensure that only fine cinder is used nearer the surface. A cricket club in a Kent coastal town laid a wicket in accordance with a normal specification. After playing upon it for a season games were marred early in the second season by accidents to batsmen through the ball lifting alarmingly and suddenly for no apparent reason. The wicket looked true and well prepared but on inspection it was found that the cinders used to assist drainage had been badly graded, with the result that large pieces were constantly working through the turf, causing an untrue surface. It was necessary to relay the square, after removing the cinder layer, and replacing with well-graded material.

SOWING SEEDS. On a clean, well-prepared, perfectly level and true surface, sowing lawn grass seeds is recommended in preference to laying turves and the following mixtures are suggested:

    (a) 70 per cent Chewing's fescue
        30 per cent Brown top

or, when Brown top is in short supply:

    (b) 90 per cent Chewing's fescue
        10 per cent Brown top

As an alternative, the inclusion of crested dogstail is suggested, for this grass is hardwearing and produces a good fibrous root system. A prescription composed of the following species will be found satisfactory:

    (c) 50 per cent Chewing's fescue
        20 per cent Creeping red fescue (S.59)
        20 per cent Crested dogstail
        10 per cent Brown top

TREATMENT FOLLOWING SOWING. When the seedling sward is one and a half to two inches high, it should be rolled lightly, and then cut with the machine set high when the grasses reach a height of three or four inches. The motor mower may be used upon the outfield, but for the table, scything or hand-mowing are advised.

Subsequent treatment of the seedling sward will follow the normal technique until it is established and prepared for play.

TURFING THE CRICKET SQUARE. Care must be taken in the selection of turves, for a springy matted sward is not required, nor should there be a preponderance of broad-bladed grasses. Species that can be mown closely to form a true surface, and produce an abundant fibrous root system are desirable. The scarcity of supplies of suitable turves renders seeding superior to turfing, if time is not the deciding factor.

Maintenance

THE SQUARE

For the production of a true, even surface marl is used extensively, supplies usually being obtained from Nottinghamshire and Leicestershire. Marl is applied alone or mixed with top-spit loam and if a mixture is decided upon is it suggested that when applied to a table for the first time one part marl to two parts loam is used. Top-spit loam off yellow clay is preferred. In subsequent years the loam content can be increased and a dressing of one part marl and three parts loam given.

Marl and loam should be sifted through a one-sixteenth straight-wire sieve. The grasses should be cut prior to dressing and to assist even distribution the area to be treated should be divided into strips three yards wide by means of pegs and strings. To avoid damage to the surface in the vicinity of the square use a barrow with rubber wheels or lay down planks. The dressing should be scattered with a shovel to not more than a depth of a quarter of an inch and worked into the soil with the back of a rake. After about a month the dressing will have disappeared and a further application can be made at the same rate. 'Marling' is usually carried out during November and December as climatic conditions allow.

MOWING. On established cricket squares mowing should commence as early as possible, setting the machine high and gradually lowering the cut as the season advances. Cricket wickets, when prepared for play, should be cut closely, for a wicket carrying too much grass can nullify the effects of otherwise good preparation.

RAKING. Routine raking with a wire rake should precede mowing to encourage the grasses to tiller.

WATERING. It is essential that a water supply be available for a good wicket cannot be made unless the surface is well watered. The sprinkler should be used early in the year providing there is no fear of frost, for a cricket table will deteriorate if allowed to become dry as a result of drying winds in March and April.

ROLLING. A cricket wicket more closely resembles a starched shirt front than a garden lawn, and it must be consolidated by heavy rolling when the soil is wet. Rollers weighing from twenty to thirty hundredweights are commonly used and rolling should commence as soon as the winter breaks, and continue during the playing season.

REPAIRS. During play the turf in the vicinity of the popping and return creases will become worn by batsmen and bowlers. A fast bowler can dig a considerable pit with his front foot and the marks of a normal bowler's run up are usually visible after the game. The practice of marking the beginning of the bowler's run by scraping the soil with the boot should be discouraged, and discs should be provided which can be pegged into the turf by the bowler.

To repair a wicket after play it is essential that work should begin as quickly as possible. Worn areas between popping and return creases should be returfed with turf from a turf nursery. Seeds should be sown on less worn parts of the bowler's run up, and it is a good plan to 'prepare' grass seeds in advance. Sacks should be laid in a shed and covered with half an inch of fine sifted soil, upon which lawn grass seeds of a suitable mixture should be sown. When the grasses commence to germinate, showing a white sprout, soil and seeds should be collected in buckets and taken and used for repairs.

TREATMENT AT THE CLOSE OF SEASON. The effects of continual heavy rolling should be corrected by forking and it is recommended that a hollow-pronged fork be used, brushing the wads of soil into the sward after they are ejected.

Marl should be applied as already recommended, working the dressing into the sward with the back of a rake or a straight-edge.

Where worms are troublesome, de-worming with a reliable worm-killer is advised, for a first-class wicket cannot be maintained on a worm-infested soil. Lawn grass seeds should be sown where the turf is weak and thin, sowing the seeds upon a raked surface, covering with fine soil and making firm with a light roller.

An application of a selective weed-killer should be made prior to sowing lawn grass seeds where weeds are troublesome.

FERTILIZER TREATMENT. The application of quick-acting nitrogenous fertilizers is not recommended and a dressing of

$\frac{1}{2}$ cwt. steamed bone flour
$\frac{1}{2}$ cwt. dried blood
$\frac{1}{4}$ cwt. calcined sulphate of iron
$1\frac{1}{2}$ cwt. finely sifted compost

is suggested for a table 30 yards square. The first application should be made as soon as repairs are complete. Fertilizers can be distributed by hand or by means of a fertilizer distributor.

In early April a second application should be made, applying:

1 cwt. steamed bone flour
1 cwt. dried blood
$\frac{1}{2}$ cwt. sulphate of potash
$2\frac{1}{2}$ cwt. finely sifted compost

During June to early July a third dressing is suggested and the following is recommended:

$\frac{1}{2}$ cwt. steamed bone flour
$\frac{1}{2}$ cwt. dried blood
1 cwt. finely sifted compost

Fertilizers and compost should be bulked prior to broadcasting.

THE OUTFIELD

Mowing should commence as early as climatic conditions allow, topping the grasses and then gradually lowering the cut. Where a high weed population exists, treatment with selective weed-killers is advised.

Spike rolling should be regarded as a routine operation and should continue throughout the year. If hockey is played on the outfield during the winter months, spiking is essential or the sward will deteriorate.

While not so closely mown, and therefore not likely to become so exhausted as the table, the outfield should be dressed with fertilizer each year. An application of general fertilizer, made during the spring, is advised—applying by means of a fertilizer-distributor. If selective weed-killers are applied, pre-treatment with sulphate of ammonia at $1\frac{1}{2}$ cwt. to the acre is recommended in preference to a balanced fertilizer. It is advisable to bulk sulphate of ammonia with sand or sterilized soil prior to application.

Fungal diseases on the table and outfield are normally not troublesome, but when these and insect pests appear prompt remedial measures must be taken.

Practice wickets should receive identical treatment to that carried out upon the playing table, and turf nurseries also should receive the same dressings of fertilizers and selective weed-killers.

B. Bowls

The game is played under two codes, the rink game more popular in the south, and the crown game played extensively in the north, but also played in some parts of southern England.

The rink game is probably most popular, being played on a flat-surfaced green, 42 yards square which allows for six rinks 7 yards wide. The size of both rink and green varies but most County Bowling Associations stipulate that affiliated clubs must have greens not less than 40 yards long. The width in such circumstances is not defined and many clubs play upon two-, three- or four-rink greens according to the demand of their membership.

Making a New Green

Making a bowling green is skilled work and is usually entrusted to specialists. The standard bowling green specification has been subject

13. Sports Centre, Southampton

14a. Golf course fairway and rough before reinstatement

14b. Twelve months later

to a great deal of adverse criticism but it must be realized that bowlers require:

(a) A true and stable surface.

(b) A green which will dry out quickly after rain, and on which dangers of weed invasion are foreseen and dealt with, and worms are discouraged.

Greens constructed as they are to-day appear to meet these demands and the only criticisms are that the insistence upon high grass banks puts additional work upon the greenkeeper. The height of the bank could with advantage be reduced to 12 inches in place of the customary 18 inches. In some cases the foundation causes such rapid drying that unless watering is resorted to early and maintained, the turf deteriorates rapidly.

THE CONSTRUCTION OF A GREEN

Excavate the site to a depth of 12 inches and put in a 4-inch drain at the base of the ditch. To provide a fall, sink the drain 6 inches below the soil after excavation and slope it down to 8 inches below this level on the opposite side to an outlet drain. Two-inch drains should now be laid in parallel lines 15 to 20 feet apart, according to the nature of the soil. These intermediate drains should be provided with a fall to the 4-inch drain laid below the foundation of the ditch.

The soil should be treated with lead arsenate powder at the rate of 2 oz. to the square yard to destroy worms.

THE FOUNDATION. On heavy clay soils a layer of broken brick or concrete hardcore 4 inches deep should be put in and rammed hard, but on lighter soil, boiler ashes carefully laid and rammed firm can be substituted. The same quantities should be put into the ditch, and ditch boards having been fixed previously and kept in position by means of 'spreaders'. A layer of rough ash 3 inches deep can now be introduced followed by a further 3 inches of fine ash. These should be rammed to a true level. It is important that the ashes should be graded in this way, for large ash in the top layer will interfere with the pricking or forking as an aid to turf maintenance. Dry summers have from time to time caused bowlers seriously to think of the advisability of securing greater moisture retention, and the incorporation of finely sifted loam with the fine ash in the proportion of 2 parts fine ash to 1 part finely sifted loam is recommended. Soil and ash should be thoroughly mixed before introduction. It is now a matter of opinion as to whether the turf should be floated upon a layer of sand from 1 to 2 inches deep or laid directly on

M   177

to the fine ash. If it is decided to lay on sand, then it would appear unnecessary to provide more than an inch layer, dressing this with dried blood at the rate of 1 oz. per square yard.

TURF. 'Cumberland' turf is regarded with enormous respect by bowlers and a 'Cumberland' is the aristocrat of greens. Samples of sea-washed turf from various parts of Great Britain appear to be equally as good as 'Cumberland' and they will most likely be used in larger quantities as their merits become known. The turves are usually cut in 12-inch squares and boxed to a uniform thickness of $1\frac{1}{4}$ inches.

They should be laid in diagonal courses and made firm with a turfing mallet.

TREATMENT FOLLOWING LAYING. When the turf has been laid it should be dressed with sand and fertilizer, applying 1 oz. of dried blood per square yard, and mixing it prior to the application with the sand in the proportion of 1 part fertilizer to 3 or 4 parts sand, working in with a dragbrush.

SOWING LAWN GRASS SEEDS.

The following prescriptions are suggested:

    (a) 50 per cent Chewing's fescue
           25 per cent Cumberland marsh creeping fescue
           25 per cent Brown top

or when brown top is in short supply:

    (b) 65 per cent Chewing's fescue
           25 per cent Cumberland marsh creeping fescue
           10 per cent Brown top

The foundation should be prepared in the same way as for turfing with the addition of a 3-inch layer of good finely sifted top-spit sterilized loam, to which a dressing of general fertilizer at the rate of 2 oz. per square yard should be given. This should be rolled firm and perfectly level. Seeds should be sown and cross-sown at the rate of 2 oz. per square yard, the soil raked to cover the seeds and then rolled to consolidate.

CROWN GREENS

Play upon this type of green takes place in any direction, transverse and diagonal, but the general construction principles follow those already outlined for the rink type of game. The surface of the crown green describes a parabola with a maximum rise of 10 inches in the centre above the level of the corners. To allow for this, the inside ditch boards will have to be five inches higher in the centre than at the corners. Banks and verges are not normally provided.

MAINTENANCE. The popularity of the 'Cumberland' or sea-washed green is due not so much to the high quality of the strains of creeping red fescue which normally form the major proportion of the sward but to the nature of the soil upon which they are growing. This tenacious earth permits ease in laying and provides a true surface for the game. Most samples are covered with a fine silt layer under the grasses and it is found that as this layer disappears the character of the sward changes.

It is a mistake to dress sea-washed turf with quick-acting nitrogenous fertilizers for this will cause a serious reduction in the fescue population. 'Cumberland' or sea-washed greens are known to deteriorate when laid inland and various reasons have been suggested. The crux of the problem would appear to lie in an incorrect fertilizer treatment. These grasses do not require forcing; a horse brought from poor pasture and suddenly fed with a corn diet will become bloated and this must be constantly borne in mind when feeding sea-washed turf.

Three applications of fertilizers annually are usually sufficient to maintain a green laid with sea-washed turf or produced from seed. These applications might be:

No. 1. In April
    1 cwt. steamed bone flour
    1 cwt. dried blood
    ½ cwt. sulphate of potash
    2½ cwt. finely sifted compost

No. 2. In June
    ½ cwt. steamed bone flour
    ½ cwt. dried blood
    1 cwt. finely sifted compost

No. 3. In August
    ½ cwt. steamed bone flour
    ½ cwt. dried blood
    ¼ cwt. calcined sulphate of iron
    1½ cwt. finely sifted compost

The materials should be bulked, applied after forking and watered in gently.

WATERING
It has been mentioned earlier that the standard bowling green specification is designed to ensure rapid drainage and therefore during a dry

period, greens can suffer alarmingly. Watering is often delayed until too late in the season and the turf is so badly checked that recovery is difficult. Should continued dry weather occur in the spring, watering is essential. The method of application on most greens is by special irrigators designed for bowling greens or by the hose-and-sack method, see page 166.

MOWING

Weather conditions will decide when mowing should commence but as soon as possible in the early spring the green should be swept and then mown with a machine set high, topping the grasses. Mowing continues during the spring and summer, increasing or decreasing in frequency as a result of climatic conditions, but twice or thrice a week is an average with a maximum of four times a week during May and June.

In conjunction with mowing, scything is advised three times a year to destroy the undergrowth which forms as a result of continued mowing and to weaken such weeds as clover and pearlwort.

ROLLING

A 10 cwt. roller can be used to obtain a true surface during the early spring but when good conditions for the game are obtained it should no longer be used. During the playing season a roller weighing 3 cwt. is preferred, and for the late summer a light wooden roller should be substituted.

MECHANICAL TREATMENT

Routine raking and brushing are advocated and forking once a month with a solid-pronged fork is advised during the playing season. In order that the run of the woods is unaffected it is recommended that forking should be diagonal across the green.

When the green is put out of play, forking with a hollow-tined fork will provide aeration when turf has become consolidated by rolling and continual play.

WEEDING

While dividing the green into strips and hand-weeding as soon as play ceases is common practice, the use of selective weed-killers is likely to increase. While pearlwort and clover are resistant to these herbicides and *Poa annua* unaffected, their resistance is perhaps only temporary as our knowledge of these growth-regulating substances grows. The use of I.P.P.C. in America for the destruction of grassy weeds and news of trials with 2-4-5 and other formulations would indicate that weed-control in the future will be less difficult than it is to-day.

COMPOSTING

In addition to the fertilizer treatment already suggested composting in the autumn following forking is advised, the compost consisting of:

> 5 parts sharp sand
> 2 parts peat

This should be applied at the rate of 2 lb. to the square yard and worked into the sward.

C. Lawn Tennis

The laying and maintenance of courts by clubs and municipal authorities has brought the game to hundreds of thousands of players in all parts of the world.

Though the uncertainty of our climate has called for an alternative to the grass court, and large numbers of hard courts have been constructed, it would appear that the good grass court is the more popular with players.

Making a New Grass Court

Tennis should be played on a true level surface, accordingly the fall of the ground must be determined by means of pegs, a straight-edge, and a spirit level. When it is necessary to cut into a bank care must be taken to provide a diversion for surplus water which will drain from the higher ground to the lower, and a pipe drain should be put in and connected to an outlet. Drainage will depend upon the site and the nature of the soil but it is most important, for a good sward cannot be maintained on a badly drained soil.

Care should be taken to ensure that the top-spit soil should be replaced after excavation and heavy retentive soils can be improved by the incorporation of fine sharp ash or sharp sand, lightly forking this into the surface.

THE SEED BED. A fine level surface should be provided by digging, hoeing, treading and rolling. Pre-treatment with general fertilizer at the rate of 2 oz. to the square yard is recommended about a fortnight before sowing. The fertilizer should be broadcast, raked in, and the soil rolled. Seeds should be sown and cross-sown at the rate of 2 oz. to the square

181

yard, raked in and rolled. If wet weather follows sowing, omit the final rolling.

Autumn sowing is preferable, although the work may have to be carried out during the spring. Whereas the fine species of *Festuca* and *Agrostis* are usually recommended for sowing tennis courts, an examination of the sward of an established court reveals that crested dogstail is well represented; and for municipal or club tennis where the sward is under continual play, the inclusion of this species is advocated. Courts which are to be played on infrequently will doubtless be satisfactory when sown with a mixture composed of:

> 70 per cent Chewing's fescue
> 30 per cent New Zealand Brown top

but for harder wear the following prescription will be found more satisfactory:

> 50 per cent Chewing's fescue
> 20 per cent Crested dogstail
> 30 per cent New Zealand Brown top

When smooth-stalked meadow-grass is available there is ample evidence that it may find favour for inclusion in a mixture to form a sward for tennis. Its ability to grow under continuous treading and its powers of recovery have already been described, and as the base lines of most courts are denuded of grasses at the end of a playing season or before, the harder-wearing species must be considered. Leafy perennial rye-grass of the Aberystwyth strain S.23 is also more likely to stand up to heavy punishment than the finer grasses, and in association with a true level surface a prescription composed as follows would at least stand hard wear:

> 20 per cent Perennial rye-grass (S.23)
> 20 per cent Crested dogstail
> 10 per cent Smooth-stalked meadow-grass
> 40 per cent Chewing's fescue
> 10 per cent New Zealand Brown top

or in the absence of smooth-stalked meadow-grass:

> 20 per cent Perennial rye-grass (S.23)
> 20 per cent Crested dogstail
> 10 per cent Timothy (S.50)
> 40 per cent Chewing's fescue
> 10 per cent New Zealand Brown top

The treatment of the seedling sward should include rolling when the grasses are from one to two inches high, and mowing lightly when they are from three to four inches in height.

TURFING. Where good turf is available a court can be laid and played upon with the minimum delay but good lawn turves are in short supply and it is preferable to sow rather than to lay with meadow turf, entirely unsuitable for the game.

An alternative is to raise a sward from seeds in a turf nursery but few clubs have facilities, although the establishment of a nursery for the production of lawn turf for repair work should not be neglected. It is essential that the cultivation of nursery turf should be thorough, but so often plans are made to establish a turf nursery and the sward receives the minimum of attention with the result that when required the material available is unsuitable for the game and the courts deteriorate through a gradual introduction of weeds and weed-grasses.

Good nursery turf should be pre-treated prior to lifting, by fertilizer applications, and after cutting evenly weeds should be removed. Each turf should be set in position and beaten with a turf mallet, and rows should be laid with alternate spacing.

When laying is completed, top dressing with fertilizer and compost is recommended, using:

> 2 parts sifted compost
> 1 part general fertilizer

Where the turf has been taken from heavy soil an alternative dressing is:

> 4 parts sand (sharp)
> 1 part general fertilizer

Apply at the rate of $\frac{1}{2}$ lb. to the square yard and work between the joints with a brush. The operation should be completed by rolling with a light roller, moving in the direction the turves are laid, and following frost it is advisable to roll again to assist the sward to knit.

MAINTENANCE. Lawn tennis, like cricket, calls for a smooth, firm, true surface and in many respects the maintenance of tennis courts resembles the technique adopted for the production of good cricket wickets. It is obvious that with continual rolling, and this is necessary, the soil will become 'hidebound', and unless steps are taken to open the surface the sward will deteriorate. As soon as the court is put out of play, forking is recommended, using a tubular fork every third year and relying on the solid-pronged type at the end of the first and second seasons.

Base lines will be bare and it is a short-sighted policy to re-turf with turves taken from the surrounds simply because the sward is green and growing strongly. Turf cultivated for the purpose will give a better performance and it is problematical whether re-seeding would not be equally successful, providing a mixture capable of rapid establishment, and producing a hard-wearing sward, was sown. The lack of green grass on the base lines of tennis courts is a reminder that seedsmen and others have for too long allowed the requirements of the putting green to influence their judgment in recommending lawn grasses for tennis. The lawn tennis base line has more in common with the Association football goalmouth; accordingly the grasses which will withstand treading should be chosen. These include perennial rye-grass, crested dogstail, and smooth-stalked meadow-grass. When mixtures containing these species are more generally sown, either for turf nursery establishment or for repairs, there will be an increase in the sward density of these heavily worn areas.

A spiked turf-beater should be used prior to sowing for opening the soil, followed by an application of general fertilizer bulked with finely sifted soil. Sow seeds, lightly cover by raking, and finally roll with a light roller.

Rolling should cease prior to the close of the season and should not be resumed until February or March, as climatic conditions allow, when it is necessary once again to prepare the courts for play.

A slippery surface must be discouraged, and where worms are troublesome 'de-worming' with a proprietary worm-killer is recommended as conditions allow. Normally it will be a spring job as turfing or sowing will take priority upon the autumn programme.

FERTILIZERS. Three applications are suggested:

No. 1. Autumn

$\frac{1}{2}$ cwt. steamed bone flour
$\frac{1}{4}$ cwt. dried blood
$\frac{1}{4}$ cwt. calcined sulphate of iron
10 cwt. finely sifted compost

No. 2. Spring

$\frac{1}{2}$ cwt. sulphate of ammonia
$\frac{1}{4}$ cwt. superphosphate
$2\frac{1}{4}$ cwt. finely sifted compost

No. 3. Summer

$\frac{1}{4}$ cwt. steamed bone flour
$\frac{1}{4}$ cwt. dried blood
1 cwt. finely sifted compost

Fertilizers and compost should be mixed thoroughly prior to application and worked into the turf by means of a straight-edge.

WEEDS. Clover is particularly troublesome upon a tennis court as patches of the weed produce a slippery surface. Raking up and treating with selective weed-killers will secure a reduction.

FUNGAL DISEASES. Fusarium patch, dollar spot, corticium and fairy rings are likely to cause trouble, and appropriate preventative and control measures should be taken. See pages 132–36.

D. Golf

A whole book and perhaps many books could be devoted to this most important aspect of turf production and maintenance. Greenkeepers to-day have at their disposal the recommendations of research workers in all parts of the world, which combined with their own practical, and often scientific, knowledge of the requirements of the fine grasses, has resulted in a great advance in intensive turf cultivation.

Golf is universal in its popularity. New clubs will be formed and new courses designed and constructed in future years. Fortunately, the trends of golf course design are leading to the best possible type of course both from the standpoint of players and greenkeepers. Golf course architecture has had its growing pains, and though here and there some earlier efforts remain the modern architect can be relied upon to produce a design which will result in a course intriguing to play over and economical to manage. The latter is probably a factor of very great importance to those to whom the management of a club is entrusted.

The New Course

Golf courses are costly to construct and their establishment in particular localities is dependent upon certain factors:

1. Public demand.
2. Accessibility by road or rail.
3. The cost of producing a course which is dependent upon (a) the natural contours of the ground, and (b) the nature of the soil.

THE GOLF ARCHITECT. This is the practical man who has studied the subject for perhaps a lifetime and who has in all probability designed, or redesigned, many of our well-known golf courses.

When a new course is under consideration, those responsible for the scheme are well advised to visit a number of clubs and to see for themselves the general design. While it is admitted that each course should have its own characteristics, certain schemes will lend themselves more readily to particular sites than to others. The officials in charge of each club should be asked to state their views on the advantages and disadvantages of their particular course. The chairman of the green committee, the secretary, and last but by no means least, the head greenkeeper can and will, if approached in the right way, be of tremendous assistance.

THE GREEN COMMITTEE. Heaven only knows why a body of otherwise normal men consents to suffer—collectively and individually—the kicks and no ha'pence of its fellow members by serving upon this often most unpopular committee. A green committee is like a government—it sometimes receives praise for the efforts of its derided predecessor which bear fruit during its term of office, but more often it is called to task for any minor calamity which may occur.

Greenkeeping should be founded upon a long-term policy, for few schemes can be tested thoroughly on a one-year trial. The policy of a green committee should be pre-determined and followed, regardless of changes in the individual membership. This is difficult, for advisory visits to golf courses reveal that there is often a gentleman with great agricultural knowledge elected to the committee, with a result that fellow members are diffident in contradicting any proposal he may make. Fine turf production is not agriculture, and many good courses have suffered through the shifting policy of its green committee.

THE HEAD GREENKEEPER. From the point of view of turf maintenance this is the most important member of the staff of any golf course, and British greenkeepers are rightly regarded as being the best in the world.

Most of the head greenkeepers employed upon our courses have spent their lives and gained their experience working their way from posts as assistants, graduating under good heads, until they fill their present positions. The British Golf Greenkeepers' Association, of which all greenkeepers should be members, is doing much to improve the standard of greenkeeping and frequent lectures are held in London and provincial centres.

The greenkeeper must be well paid if the best type of man is to be obtained and the green committee must work with him in the closest possible way. So often experts are called in to give advice upon problems which could be solved by the greenkeeper whose opinion has not been asked for, or if given, disregarded.

Most greenkeepers enjoy the confidence of club members and such incidents are few, but nevertheless they do occur.

GOLF COURSE MAINTENANCE

It is not difficult to make recommendations for the improvement of golf courses, to suggest maintenance schemes, and to advise upon the purchase of equipment. The deciding factor is, however, a financial one and the ability to put them into practice will depend upon the income available. It is not intended in this work to describe operations in great detail as the work will be carried out by practical greenkeepers, who know their job. Recommendations and suggestions are made in the form of a programme of seasonal work, a reminder to the practical and it is hoped not without interest to the beginner or enthusiastic green committee member.

AUTUMN WORK. At the close of summer, greens will be showing signs of wear and tear, moss may be present, and the sward may not look in good general condition. During September make an application of a good balanced fertilizer, mixing this with sand in the proportion of 1 part fertilizer to 5 or 6 parts sand and work it in. Where the turf is weak and thin reinforce with grass seeds and a suitable prescription is one composed of:

> 70 per cent Chewing's fescue
> 30 per cent New Zealand Brown top

or:

> 70 per cent Chewing's fescue
> 20 per cent Cumberland marsh fescue
> 10 per cent Brown top

WORMS. During September worms are usually nearer to the surface and can be destroyed more readily. Choose suitable climatic conditions, test a small area before embarking upon extensive de-worming. Often in practice the work has to be deferred until October.

PREPARATION OF TURF IN NURSERIES. Sods will be required later for patching greens and tees. Continue mowing during September, making an application of fertilizer about the middle of the month and then leave and commence patching late in October.

Where no nursery exists, select good areas of turf on the fairways or in the rough, and work these up in the same way.

DIVOT MARKS. Although good golfers replace divots, these are often disturbed before the turf can unite, leaving scars. They should be repaired by sowing a mixture of fescues and bents, as advised for the greens. Fill the marks with soil, sow the seeds upon the surface, lightly cover with soil and then make firm.

CONSOLIDATED TURF. Greens should be forked during October and a spike roller run over the fairways. After forking, greens should be dressed with compost.

WINTER WORK. Bunkers holding water should be drained by digging sump holes to a depth of about 4 feet, filling them with stones, finishing off with cinders and then adding the sand. During wet weather tools should be cleaned, implements inspected and sent for overhauling where required.

Composts can be sieved and prepared when outdoor work is not possible. Sand boxes and flagstaffs can also be painted.

Turfing should be completed before the end of the year.

EARLY SPRING WORK. Where drainage is required and has not been carried out earlier, the months of January and February should be used to get the work completed.

Greens should be composted and a good time is from the middle until the end of February, as conditions permit. Teeing grounds should be given similar treatment.

As soon as the grasses recommence growth, mowing will begin. Do not cut too keenly; top the grasses frequently when the weather is suitable. Conditions may, however, allow the work to proceed only for a few hours each day—consequently, machines must be ready.

Weed-destruction by the use of a selective weed-killer is suggested but where the sward needs reinforcement and lawn grass seeds are to be sown, a formulation of 2 : 4-D (D.C.P.A.) is advised.

Any bare or thin places remaining on greens, fairways, or teeing grounds should be reinforced with seeds as already recommended, carrying out the work at the end of March, or as conditions allow. Where it was not possible to destroy worms in the autumn the work can be carried out at the end of March, or during April, but autumn de-worming usually fits itself more easily into the greenkeeper's programme.

SPRING WORK. Mowing has a great bearing on the quality of the sward and neglect can prove very costly. The cut can gradually be lowered and mowing may be said to be in full swing on most courses before the end of April. Frequent mowing is preferable to mowing once a week, and putting greens should be mown three or four times each week from now onwards.

A good finish is given to a green by using a ten-bladed hand mower, reducing the use of the motor mower to one cut per week. The use of a power outfit of the 'Overgreen' type will result in a saving of time and labour. With lawnmowers assembled as a 'gang' it is possible for one man to cut eighteen greens in a day. During dry weather when the surface of the green is inclined to become hard, it is often advisable to rely entirely upon hand-cutting. The grass box can be removed from all machines during the summer months, except where annual meadowgrass (*Poa annua*) is present.

SUMMER WORK. This is a difficult period—one during which a spell of dry weather or even drought may be experienced. Ample water must be available, for during a very dry summer, greens must be watered or they will deteriorate. It is essential to soak thoroughly. A few hours' watering is not enough; the soil must be well-wetted to a depth of nearly six inches.

Should any of the greens show signs of languishing during this trying period, fertilizer may be applied at any time during the summer months.

SEEDS MIXTURES. Fairways and greens are not normally subjected to excessive wear and tear and therefore a higher proportion of the finer grasses can be included.

For greens the following prescriptions are suggested:

(a) 70 per cent Chewing's fescue
    30 per cent Brown top
(b) 70 per cent Chewing's fescue
    20 per cent Cumberland marsh fescue
    10 per cent Brown top

The simple mixture of Chewing's fescue and brown top will give satisfactory results on most soils but the alternative prescription introduces the fine fescues collected from the Cumberland marshes. Seeds should be sown at the rate of 2 oz. to the square yard.

For fairways and rough the following are recommended:

(a) 25 per cent Perennial rye-grass (S.23)
    10 per cent Timothy (S.50)
    10 per cent Crested dogstail
    45 per cent Chewing's fescue
    10 per cent Brown top

or when smooth-stalked meadow-grass is available:

(b) 25 per cent Perennial rye-grass (S.23)
    10 per cent Timothy (S.50)
    10 per cent. Smooth-stalked meadow-grass
    45 per cent Chewing's fescue
    10 per cent Brown top

189

Seeds should be sown at the rate of 1½ to 2 cwt. per acre.

For teeing grounds great care must be taken in deciding upon a mixture as tees are heavily worn and the grasses must withstand treading under dry conditions in view of the rapid draining of the teeing ground.

For rapid establishment and hard wear the following prescription is likely to prove satisfactory:

50 per cent Perennial rye-grass (S.23)
20 per cent Smooth-stalked meadow-grass
10 per cent Hard fescue
10 per cent Crested dogstail
10 per cent Wood meadow-grass

Unfortunately at present smooth-stalked and wood meadow-grass are not available commercially and, therefore, an alternative suggestion is:

50 per cent Perennial rye-grass (S.23)
30 per cent Crested dogstail
20 per cent Hard fescue

The alternative prescription is likely to be worth approximately 350s. per cwt.

Seeds should be sown at the rate of 2 oz. to the square yard.

E. Parks

Lord Samuel in a contribution to the *Sunday Times*, described a walk of many miles in London's parks and reminded his readers that it was possible to escape from the busy everyday world and find almost rural peace, close to the heart of the great metropolis.

Bombed Coventry, rising Phoenix-like from the ashes, is extending its parks and providing recreation for young and old amidst verdant scenery.

At Bristol where the prows of tall ships once overhung the roadway, the old Tramways Centre has been changed beyond recognition. Gone are the noisy trams, and at the point from which they radiated are well-kept lawns and flower borders.

Manchester, Birmingham, Liverpool, Middlesbrough, Sheffield, Leeds, Nottingham, Derby and Leicester, manufacturing communities of great national importance, are among the many cities and towns where the people can enjoy to the full the restful delights which are associated with green grass, and how refreshing it is in Oldham, Rochdale and Salford to find good parks cared for by skilled horticulturists.

Time was when the park was for the few, to-day it is the possession of the many, and therefore within reasonable limits freedom of movement should be enjoyed by the people for whom our parks are maintained. The irritating notice 'Please keep off the grass' is an anachronism. Can we not move to an era when all can walk on the greensward? Parks Superintendents will no doubt complain of the wear and tear, but if the position is examined closely it will probably be found that such notices are normally required only where the public refuses to keep to winding walks when a short cut is possible, and therefore the fault would appear to lie in park design.

The park which has evolved from a private garden is likely to present turf maintenance problems of this kind, and many of our older parks were made either to meet the needs of a more leisurely age or not designed to cater for the larger public which is thronging them to-day. Parks administration in the future would render a great service to the community if, when planning our new parks and open spaces, provision is made for planting schemes which will prevent short cuts. The purpose for which the path is constructed should also receive more careful thought for if a path winds away from an exit it is not unnatural for the visitor to disregard a warning notice and to take the quickest way out. In our older parks this leads more often than not over an ornamental lawn.

Seeds mixtures will need consideration if the public is to be allowed to walk upon the turf, and while it is realized that a prescription of fine species of *Festuca* and *Agrostis* would not withstand continual treading under normal cultivation, the introduction of harder wearing grasses should assist in solving the problem.

For the broad expanse of turf where rallies, fêtes and other outdoor gatherings are held, the following mixture has been found satisfactory:

(a) 60 per cent Perennial rye-grass
   10 per cent Smooth-stalked meadow-grass
   10 per cent Crested dogstail
   10 per cent Chewing's fescue
   10 per cent Brown top

Where the soil is more water-retentive an alternative is:

(b) 60 per cent Perennial rye-grass
   10 per cent Rough-stalked meadow-grass
   10 per cent Crested dogstail
   10 per cent Chewing's fescue
   10 per cent Brown top

The absence from the market of smooth-stalked meadow-grass will call for a modification of mixture (a) but as an alternative Timothy is suggested.

Seeds should be sown at the rate of $1\frac{1}{2}$ to 2 cwt. per acre. Purely ornamental lawns may be sown with a more simple mixture of:

> 70 per cent Chewing's fescue
> 30 per cent Brown top

Reduction in the content of brown top may be called for when the species is in short supply. For lawns receiving light wear, harder wearing grasses can be combined with the fine species in the following prescription:

> 25 per cent Perennial rye-grass
> 10 per cent Timothy
> 10 per cent Crested dogstail
> 45 per cent Chewing's fescue
> 10 per cent Brown top

This mixture will produce a sward similar to that formed on a golf course fairway and will withstand reasonable wear.

F. Football and Hockey

The popularity of Association, Rugby Union and Rugby League football is confirmed by the many clubs and their multitude of supporters. Hockey, although not drawing such vast crowds, is enjoyed by players of both sexes and there are indications that providing playing facilities are made available greater numbers of players will take up the game.

FOOTBALL PITCHES FROM THE ROUGH

Through various reasons clubs are often faced with the problem of renovating a neglected playing pitch or forming a pitch from ordinary meadow-land. Finance does not allow these clubs to construct a playing pitch in the same way as a wealthier organization, accordingly they face the task often with no other help than the efforts of the playing members.

Football should be played upon a true level surface and if a meadow is converted for the game, drainage, furrows or ridges will have to be levelled, stripping the turf and moving the soil from the higher to the lower ground. When possible the work should commence in autumn and the turf be rolled after laying and rolled again following frosty weather.

15a. Spring Rake Scarifier Unit

15b. Medium weight Gang Rollers

16a. Hand Turf-Piercing Machine

16b. Piercing Implements in action

In the spring, as conditions allow, the grasses should be scythed or 'topped' with the mower set high, and treated with a selective weed-killer of the 2: 4-D (D.C.P.A.) group during March or early April. The actual time of application will depend upon soil temperature for if the soil is slow to warm it is advisable to defer the application.

In order to produce a softer type of weed growth, pre-treatment with sulphate of ammonia fourteen days before weed-killing is advised. The fertilizer should be distributed at the rate of 1 cwt. to the acre and mixed with finely sifted soil or sand to act as a carrier in the proportion of one part fertilizer to five parts by weight of soil or sand.

Treatment with a selective weed-killer of the 2: 4-D (D.C.P.A.) group will not normally inhibit the germination and growth of grass seeds sown to renovate where the turf is weak or thin; but it is suggested that the advice and recommendations of the manufacturers be sought and followed.

After seeding, dress with finely screened soil, allowing forty cubic yards for the playing area. The application can be made when the grasses have been mown for the first time and the soil should be worked into the turf with the back of a rake or a straight edge.

Mowing should continue during the summer months but no attempt should be made to cut closely. The grasses should be left about three inches long until about a month before the season opens, when the cut should be taken lower until the sward is mown to the desired height. Association football pitches are usually mown more closely to suit the needs of the game than Rugby football grounds where the grasses are left longer.

Heavy rolling is not recommended but about a fortnight before the season opens rolling to firm up the surface is advised, rolling again a week later.

MAKING NEW PITCHES FROM SEEDS

When funds are available, making a pitch on a proved foundation with adequate drainage and sowing a suitable seeds mixture is the ideal.

Clay pipe or porous pipe drains should be laid approximately 15 inches below the surface, using 6-inch pipes for the mains and 2- or 3-inch pipes for the spurs or laterals.

Graded cinders should then be introduced to a depth of 6 inches, rolled and covered with 4 inches of good soil. This should be covered with a further inch of soil and cinders passed through a sieve with an $\frac{1}{8}$ inch mesh. The site should now be topped with 4 inches of good, finely screened soil and rolled to make a firm seed bed. It is of great

N   193

importance that the surface soil should be firm for lawn grass seeds germinate more freely than when sown on unconsolidated land, particularly when a period of dry weather follows sowing.

SEEDS MIXTURES. Probably no sward receives harder winter wear than that which forms a football pitch for it is played upon for more than eight months of the year, consolidated beyond description, and continually torn by the boots of the players. In the circumstances it is not surprising that the finer grasses are generally unsuitable for inclusion in the mixture and if an examination of the badly worn areas is made at the close of a playing season it will be observed that where grasses have survived they are usually perennial rye-grass, smooth-stalked meadow-grass, and crested dogstail.

Accordingly for sowing football pitches the following mixtures are recommended.

In the absence of smooth-stalked meadow-grass:

(a) 80 per cent Perennial rye-grass (S.23)
    20 per cent Crested dogstail

(b) 70 per cent Perennial rye-grass (S.23)
    20 per cent Crested dogstail
    10 per cent Timothy (S.50)

When smooth-stalked meadow-grass is available:

(c) 60 per cent Perennial rye-grass (S.23)
    20 per cent Smooth-stalked meadow-grass
    10 per cent Crested dogstail
    10 per cent Timothy (S.50)

(d) 80 per cent Perennial rye-grass (S.23)
    20 per cent Smooth-stalked meadow-grass

Hockey is also very exacting upon the sward and although there may be less wear and tear than that caused by football the same mixtures are suggested.

It may be argued that hockey is played with a smaller ball which normally moves over the surface of the turf and therefore fine grasses are demanded. Experience has proved that these fine grasses cannot withstand winter games of this type and if sown will soon disappear. Perennial rye-grass, smooth-stalked meadow-grass and crested dogstail are pre-eminent for winter games and their value will be appreciated more fully when better known. That the fescues and bents are desirable for golf greens and fairways is not disputed, but golf and hockey cannot be compared as far as wear and tear are concerned.

The golf course sward should not be the model for the recreation ground which will be called upon to support a full winter programme. The policy should be to sow hard-wearing grasses and to continue to renovate with them until a sward is established which will defy the hardest wear.

TURFING. A football club on the outskirts of London purchased a site which had been used as gravel pits. During the war years, debris from bombed areas was dumped with an assortment of bricks, unexploded bombs, scrap iron and broken bottles. Without advice this club hired bulldozers to level the area and after spending a considerable sum in an effort to construct a sports arena, called in experts. The club was in a difficult position as the lease upon its existing ground had expired with no prospect of renewal. After work had been in progress for a month an expert inspection was made. The contractors had worked hard to create a level surface for a football pitch but in April the work was far from complete. It was the intention of the football club to sow with lawn grass seeds and to play upon the pitch in October. An inspection revealed that broken bottles were near to the surface and even if the land was fallowed and then sown, delaying the opening of the ground, there was insufficient good top-spit soil to support a sward and serious injury to players was likely from the debris near to the surface.

The impracticability of sowing was stressed and the necessity of importing top-spit loam recommended with a further suggestion that turfing was desirable in view of the short space of time left to them. Had this club called upon experts at an earlier date a considerable saving would have been effected.

Laying turf can save time providing suitable turf is available, but it is a mistake for clubs to purchase meadow turf which may contain grasses incapable, when closely mown, of withstanding the hard wear of winter games. If good turf composed of hard-wearing grasses cannot be obtained, seeding is advised. The most opportune time for turfing new football pitches is during the autumn but a large number of pitches are laid with turves in the spring in order that play can commence the following autumn. Each turf should be examined before laying, removing weeds. Rolling after laying is advised and the turf should be rolled again if lifted by frost. When laying is completed dress with finely screened soil allowing about fifty cubic yards for a full-sized playing area.

MAINTENANCE—FOOTBALL

The extension of the playing season from late August until mid-May restricts the time in which adequate renovation can be carried out. At the end of a playing season most grounds are denuded of grasses in the goalmouth areas, particularly upon Association football grounds, and often the centre of the pitch supports only a very sparse sward.

In a limited time, approximately three months, seeds must be sown and growth encouraged so that play can resume in late August. Nothing calls for greater skill upon the part of a groundsman than this type of renovation carried out during a period of the year which is considered unsuitable for seed sowing, and speed is essential if success is to be obtained.

As soon as the season ends work must begin. The surface will be 'hidebound' and in the goalmouth areas on Association grounds and on other parts of the field where the sward is non-existent, the soil should be disc-harrowed or broken up with a rotary cultivator. So great is the consolidation that on heavy clays a heavy set of tandem disc-harrows is preferred. As the soil is broken up general fertilizer at the rate of 2 oz. to the square yard should be applied and harrowed in.

The soil should then be rolled, seeds sown by 'fiddle', barrow or by hand, followed by peg harrowing so that they are lightly covered, and then rolled with a medium roller.

If dry weather follows sowing, water should be resorted to, where this is available, but where there are no facilities the sward is at the mercy of the weather. Sowing on a firm seed bed is emphasized however, for this enables the germinating grasses to survive during dry periods.

When the grasses are about two inches high they should be rolled lightly, providing the soil is not holding excessive moisture, and 'topped' with the mower when about three or four inches high. The cut should be lowered as mowing is repeated until cut to the desired length.

A week or so before the season opens the pitch should be rolled with the heavy roller to form a true surface but continued rolling is not recommended.

Over-consolidation is responsible for the bad wearing of most football grounds and this must be counteracted by spiking or piercing with the spiked roller or turf-piercing machine. Neglect to spike or pierce will prove fatal and spiking as a routine operation is recommended twice or three times a week.

During the playing season when the turf is endeavouring to withstand the demands of the game, fertilizers are required, yet their application is often delayed until play ceases. One or two applications of general fertilizer during the spring will assist a 'tired' sward. Quick-acting nitrogenous fertilizers should be avoided for these tend to produce a soft 'flush' of grasses incapable of withstanding hard wear. A good proprietary general grass fertilizer will feed without forcing. An application can be made in late February if conditions allow and repeated early in April, but when the season does not permit an early application a dressing during March at the rate of 2 cwt. per acre is suggested. When two applications are made apply at half this rate on each occasion.

Selective weed-killing is often advocated when the season closes but care must be taken in selecting a suitable type, for the growth of the grasses may be inhibited. An Association football club in Northants applied a Methoxone-containing-powder after closing its ground for play on 30th April and then planned to sow lawn grass seeds after an interval of a fortnight. This club was advised that sowing would probably result in failure. Had advice been sought before treating the sward it would probably have resulted in the club applying a selective weed-killer containing the ethyl ester or amine salt of 2, 4-D. (D.C.P.A.) which would not have affected adversely the germination or subsequent growth of the grass seeds.

TOUCH LINES. It is the modern practice in Association football for linesmen to officiate upon what is known as the diagonal system, each linesman controlling half of the field and as the tendency appears to be for each official to concentrate on the half of the field to the right of the centre line it is noticeable that turf near the side lines is denuded early in the playing season.

It is suggested that to remedy this constant wear, on alternate weeks linesmen should control the area on the left of the centre line and in this way wear would be distributed. A notice in the dressing-room of the officials concerned would remind linesmen of the system in operation. It may sound revolutionary to suggest such rules, but it would appear to be high time to consider the groundsman and his work in relation to the well-being of the game.

MAINTENANCE—HOCKEY

The season usually begins later and ends earlier than football and in the circumstances more time is allowed for renovation, the programme for which should follow very closely that suggested for a football pitch.

Glossary of Botanical Terms

⫸⫸⫸⫸ ⦿ ⫷⫷⫷⫷

ACHENE: A dry fruit which is indehiscent and contains one seed.

ACULEATE: Having prickles.

ACUTE: The apex of a leaf is described as acute when it forms an acute angle or tapers to a point.

ALTERNATE: Branches, or leaves, are alternate when one proceeds from each node; one on one side and the next above or below on the opposite side of the stem.

AMPLEXICAUL: Leaves are so described when the sessile base of the blade clasps the stem horizontally.

ANTHER: Part of a stamen which contains the pollen borne on a filament, and divided into two pouches or cells.

AQUATIC: A plant which grows in water.

ASCENDING: Stems which spread horizontally at the base and then turn upwards and become erect.

AURICLES: The two lateral lobes at the base of a leaf.

AURICULATE: When the auricles are pointed, a leaf is called auriculate.

AXIL: The angle formed by a leaf and a branch.

BISEXUAL: Stamens male and pistil female in the same flower.

BLADE: An ordinary leaf consists of a flat blade or lamina, usually green, attached to a stem or stalk, known as a footstalk or petiole.

BRACTS: A name given to the upper leaves of a plant in flower, when they differ from the stem leaves in size, shape and colour, or arrangement. They are usually smaller and more sessile.

BRACTEATE: Having bracts.

BRACTEOLES: When one or two last bracts under a flower differ in size, shape and arrangements from the other bracts they are known as bracteoles.

BRISTLES: Very stiff erect straight hairs.

CAESPITOSE: Tufted.

CALYX: A collective name for the sepals.

CAPILLARY: Hair-like.

CAPITATE: When several sessile or nearly sessile flowers are collected together into a compact cluster or head.

CAPSULE: A dry pod which is dehiscent.

198

CARBOHYDRATES: Compounds which form the largest part of the body of plants. The chief carbohydrates are, sugars, starch, insulin, cellulose and pestosans.

CARPEL: Parts of the pistil, containing one or more seeds.

CARYOPSIS: The peculiar fruits of certain orders are given special names. Those of Gramineæ, Caryopsis or Grain.

CAUDEX: The axis of a plant consisting of stem and root.

CAULINE: Leaves which are borne on a distinct stalk.

CHLOROPHYLL: The green colouring matter, most abundant in the cells immediately below the surface of leaves and young bark.

CILIATE: When leaves are bordered with fine hairs or hair-like teeth.

COMPOUND LEAF: When leaves are divided to the midrib or petiole.

COMPOUND UMBEL: When each ray bears a partial umbel or umbellule.

COMPRESSED: Leaves are compressed when more or less flattened laterally.

CONFLUENT: Anthers occasionally have only one cell. When this results from the disappearance of the partition between two closely contiguous cells these cells are termed confluent.

CORDATE: Heart-shaped.

COROLLA: A collective name for the petals.

CORYMB or CORYMBOSE: An inflorescence is so described when the branches, starting from different points, attain the same level.

CREEPING: When stems emit roots at their nodes.

CRENATE: When the teeth on the margin of a leaf are regular and blunt or rounded.

CULM: A name given to the stem of grasses and sedges.

CUNEATE: A description used for a leaf which is broadest above the middle or wedge shaped.

CUSPIDATE: The summit of a leaf is cuspidate or acuminate when suddenly narrowed at the top forming a rigid point.

CYME: A branched flower cluster, where the central flower opens first. Subsequent flower branches usually grow longer than the main.

DECIDUOUS: When scales, sepals, petals and leaves fall in season.

DECUMBENT: Used for stems when they spread horizontally or nearly so, but become upright at the apex.

DECURRENT: When the edges of the leaf are continued down the stem to form raised lines or ridges as the petiole of a thistle.

DECUSSATE: When leaves or branches are opposite but each pair at right angles to the pairs above and below.

DEHISCENCE: Anthers open to let out pollen and fruits open to discharge seeds.

DELTOID: Like the Greek letter △.

DENTATE: More usually applied to the toothed margin of a leaf.

DEPRESSED: Leaves are depressed when more or less flattened vertically.

DIADELPHOUS: When stamens are united into two clusters.

DIANDROUS: Having two stamens.

DICLINOUS: The flowers of a plant are said collectively to be diclinous or unisexual when they are all either male or female.

DICHOTOMOUS: When the branch forks into two, then each branch divides again.

DICOTYLEDONOUS: Having two cotyledons or seed leaves.

DIDYMOUS: Stems, fruit, tubers and other parts when not flattened like ordinary leaves are didymous when slightly two-lobed, with rounded obtuse lobes.

DIDYNAMOUS: When there are four stamens, one pair longer than the other as in most Labiatae.

DIFFUSE: Stems are so described when they spread along the ground and are loosely branched.

DIGITATE: Like the fingers of a hand. Applied to compound leaves like the horse chestnut.

DIOECIOUS: When the male and female organs are on separate plants.

DORSAL: On the back or attached thereto.

DUCTS: Tubular vessels marked with lines or dots.

EAR: A form of the spike.

EMARGINATE: Notched or decidedly indented at the extremity.

ENSIFORM: Shaped like a broad sword.

ENTIRE: Undivided, with even margin.

EPIDERMIS: The outer skin

EXOTIC: Not native.

EXSERTED: Extending beyond. When stamens are longer than the corolla.

FAMILY: A collection of genera.

FASICLED or FASICULATE: When two or three branches or leaves proceed from the same node on the same side of the stem.

FILAMENT: The stalk of an anther.

FILIFORM: Capillary or hair-like.

FIMBRIATED: Fringed.

FLOCCULENT: Having a woolly or downy covering.

FLORETS: The small flowers collected into a head in composite plants.

FOLIACEOUS: Leaf-like.

FRUCTIFICATION: Fruiting body.

FURCATE: Forked.

GAMO: United or fused.

GENUS: A collection of related species.

GLABROUS: Without hairs.

GLANDS: Minute raised dots, small wart-like organs, situated below or on the surface or in the hairs of plants for the secretion of fluids.

GLAUCOUS: Having a bluish or sea-green bloom upon the foliage.

GLOBOSE: Globe shaped, spherical.

GLUMES: The bracts enclosing the flowers of grasses.

GUARD-CELLS: Small pores through which gaseous exchange takes place, have their opening controlled by special guard-cells.

HABIT: General characters which are apparent to the eye, e.g. size, colour, arrangement of leaves, etc.

HABITAT: The natural home.

HALOPHYTE: A plant enjoying a saline environment.

HARDY: Enduring without protection.

HASTATE: When the points of the auricles diverge to resemble a halberd.

HEREDITY: The study of inheritance.

HERMAPHRODITE: Bisexual.

HISPID: Hirsute, with long distinct hairs.

HOST: A plant supporting a parasite.

HYBRIDS: The progeny of a cross between two different species.

HYDROPONICS: The soil-less cultivation of plants in water to which nutrients are added.

HYPO-: Below, i.e. hypocotyl: the axis of an embryo below the cotyledons.

IMBRICATE, IMBRICATED: Overlapping.

IMPERFECT: When certain parts are missing.

INDEHISCENT: When anthers do not open to let out pollen, or fruits do not open to discharge seeds.

INDIGENOUS: A native of the country.

INFERIOR: Situated below an organ, i.e. an ovary is inferior when the other floral organs are situated above it.

INFLORESCENCE: A flowering branch with a single flower, or a collection of flowers.

INVOLUCEL: The secondary partial involucre of a compound umbel.

INVOLUCRE: The collection of bracts surrounding a head of flowers.

INVOLUTE: With the leaf margins rolled inwards.

IRREGULAR: A flower which cannot be halved in any plane.

KEEL: Two loosely united petals of a leguminous flower. The ridge or the lower surface of the leaf blades of some grasses.

GLOSSARY OF BOTANICAL TERMS

LAMINA: The blade of a leaf.

LANCEOLATE: A leaf is so described when it tapers at both ends or when it has an acute tip and is broadest some distance from the base.

LATEX: The milky gelatinous fluid exuded by certain plants.

LEGUME: A pod.

LEMMA: The outer palea or outer flowering glume of a grass.

LIGULE: A small membranous appendage.

LINEAR: A leaf is so described when it is several times longer than broad.

LUNEATE: Crescent shaped.

LYRATE: Having small lower lobes but the terminal large and rounded. Like a lyre.

MEMBER: A structure of a plant, i.e. a leaf, sepal, petal or stamen.

MOLLIS: Pubescent or soft.

MONO-: One in composition, e.g. monocotyledon, a plant with one cotyledon.

MUCRONATE: When the midrib of a leaf is produced beyond the apex to form a small point.

MUTATION: A change in a plant or animal during its life history.

MUTANT: A new type produced by mutation.

MULTI-: Many.

MYCELIUM: The vegetative part of a fungus.

MYURUS: Tapering like a rat's tail.

NATIVE: Indigenous.

NATURAL ORDER: A collection of families.

NAVICULAR: Boat-shaped.

NECTORY: A small receptacle holding nectar or honey.

NERVE: A prominent rib or vein.

NODE: A point of the stem or its branches at which leaves, or leaf buds, are given off.

NODULE: A small outgrowth of irregular shape.

NUT: An indehiscent fruit containing one seed. The outermost covering becomes hardened.

OB-: A prefix denoting reversed, or opposite, e.g. Ob-ovate: inversely egg-shaped. Ob-cordate: inversely cordate.

OBTUSE: Terminating in a blunt point.

ORBICULAR: Circular.

OSMOSIS: The diffusion or passage of liquids and solutions of substances through membranes in which no visible openings are present.

OVARY: The female portion of the flower, which contains seeds.

OVATE: Egg-shaped.

PALEA: Palea, Pales, or Chaff are the inner bracts or scales in Compositæ, Gramineæ, and some other orders of plants.

PALMATE: See Digitate.

PANICLE: An inflorescence is a panicle when the axis is divided into branches bearing two or more flowers.

PAPPUS: A ring of hairs or scales around the top of a fruit.

PEDATE: The leaflets, segments, lobes, veins of leaves are pedate when the division is at first ternate but the two outer branches are forked and then fork again, and so on, with all the branches close together at the base somewhat resembling the foot of a bird.

PEDICEL: The last branch of an inflorescence supporting a single flower.

PEDICELLATE: On a pedicel.

PEDUNCLE: The stalk of a solitary flower or of an inflorescence.

PEDUNCULATE: On a peduncle.

PELTATE: In a peltate leaf the stalk is attached to the under surface instead of proceeding from the lower edge of the blade. It is usually nearer the lower edge but sometimes in the very centre of the blade.

PENTA-: Five in composition.

PERENNIAL: After flowering the whole or part of the plant lives through the winter and produces fresh flowers another season. In herbaceous perennials the greater part of the plant dies after flowering, leaving only a small perennial portion called the Stock or Caudex close to or within the earth.

PERIANTH: A floral envelope which usually encloses the stamens and pistil when young, expanding to expose them to view when fully formed.

PETIOLE: The foot stalk by means of which the leaf blade or lamina is attached to the stem.

PHYLLODIUM: A flat petiole with no blade.

PILOSE: When the surface or outer skin of an organ is thinly sprinkled with rather long simple hairs.

PINNATE: When there are several leaflets succeeding each other on each side of the mid-rib or petiole compared with the branches of a feather.

PISTIL: The whole collection of carpels is known as the gynaecium or pistil of the flower.

PLUMULE: The future bud within the base of the cotyledons.

PROLIFEROUS: A plant is said to be viviparous or proliferous when adventitious buds are produced in the place of flowers or seeds.

PROSTRATE: When a stems lies very close to the ground.

PULVENATE: Cushion shaped.

PUNCTIFORME: Like a point or dot.

RACE: If a variety is reproduced true from seeds it is often called a race.

RACEME: An inflorescence is so described when the flowers are borne on pedicles along a single undivided axis or rachis.

RACHIS: The portion of the peduncle extending from the first ramification to the last, or the axis of the inflorescence.

RADICAL: Leaves are so described when they arise so close to the rhizome or stock as to appear to proceed from it.

RADICLE: The embryonic base of the future root.

RECEPTACLE: The extremity of the peduncle upon which the corolla, stamens and ovary are inserted.

RENIFORM: A reniform leaf is broader than long, broadly cordate at the base, with rounded auricles. Literally, 'kidney-shaped'.

RETICULATE: When the smaller veins are connected together like meshes of a net.

RHIZOME: The lowest branches of a plant are sometimes underground and assume the appearance of a root, taking the name of a rhizome. A rhizome can be distinguished by the presence or production of buds.

RHOMBOIDAL: The shape of a leaf as compared with the corresponding mathematical figure. Quadrangular with the lateral angles obtuse.

RIBBED: The epidermis or outer skin is said to be ribbed or costate when marked with distinctly raised parallel lines.

ROSTRATE: Beaked.

SAGITTATE: When the leaf resembles a barbed arrow-head.

SCABROUS: The epidermis is so described when it is rough to the touch.

SCALES: Leaves very much reduced in size.

SCAPE: A leafless peduncle proceeding from the stock of the base of the stem.

SCARIOUS, SCARIOSE: Very thin, more or less transparent, yet rather stiff.

SCATTERED: Branches or leaves are scattered when arranged irregularly around the stem.

SEPALS: These are parts of the outer whorl of a flower which is known as the calyx.

SERRATE, SERRULATE: When the leaf margin is cut and the teeth are regular and pointed like a saw.

SESSILE: Leaves are said to be sessile when the base of the blade forms a vertical sheath round the stem.

SETACEOUS: Bristle-like.

SHEATHING: Leaves are said to be sheathing when the base of the blade forms a vertical sheath round the stem.

SIMPLE: Leaves are simple or entire when the blade consists of a single piece with the margin not indented.

SINUATE: The teeth of leaves are so described when broad and irregular.

SPIKELET: Ears and spikelets of grasses are forms of the spike.

SPIRIOUS: Possessing thorns.

STAMENS: Those parts of the flower which carry pollen in their anthers to fertilize the pistil.

STELLATE or ROTATE: When the petals or lobes are spread out horizontally from the base like a star or a wheel.

STEM-CLASPING: See amplexicaul.

STERILE: Barren: not producing seeds.

STIGMA: A small head or point at the top of the style or ovary.

STIPES: A stalk.

STIPULES: Leaf-like or scale-like appendages at the base of the leaf stalk or on the node of the stem.

STOCK: The portion of the stem and root which does not die.

STOLON: An annual stock which maintains communication between the annual stem and root of one year, and those of the following year.

STRIATE: When the epidermis is marked with slightly raised, parallel, longitudinal lines.

STYLE: Comes from the top of the ovary and supports the stigma.

SUBULATE: When parts of plants are thick and firm and resemble awls.

TERNATE: When three branches of leaves proceed from the same node and the same side of the stem.

TILLERING: A common mode of branching in grasses and cereals. The formation of shoots which spring from near the surface of the soil.

TOMENTOSE: Cottony, woolly.

TRIBE: The genera of an order are collected into minor groups called tribes.

TRIFID: Three-lobed.

TRIFOLIATE: A leaf with three leaflets.

TRUNCATED: When the end is cut off square.

TUBERCULATE: When the epidermis is covered with small obtuse warts.

TURBINATE: Top-shaped.

UMBEL: Flower cluster consisting of several nearly equal branches proceeding from the same point and forming a flat head; e.g. parsley.

UNCINATE: Hooked.

UNILATERAL: One-sided.

UTRICLE: When the pericarp of an achene is thin and rather loose it is often called an utricle.

VALVES: The pericarp of a capsule or pod when ripe usually splits longitudinally into valves.

VARIETY: When a large number of individuals of a species differ markedly from the others, they constitute a variety.

VIRGATE: Twiggy.

VIVIPAROUS or PROLIFEROUS: Buds producing roots which become distinct plants before separating from the parent; or if adventitious, leaf-buds are produced in place of flowers or seeds.

WARTED: See Tuberculate.

WHORLED or VERTICILLATE: When several branches or leaves proceed from the same node, arranged regularly around the stem.

Bibliography

❧❧❧❧ ⚬ ❦❦❦❦

ARMSTRONG, S. F., *British Grasses* (Cambridge University Press).

BEALE, R., *Lawns for Sports* (Simpkin Marshall, 1924).

BENTHAM & HOOKER, *Handbook to the British Flora* (L. Reeve & Co., 1924).

BUCKMAN, JAMES, *The Natural History of British Meadow & Pasture Grasses* (Hamilton, Adams & Co., 1858).

CLOUSTON, D., *The Establishment & Care of Fine Turf* (Wyllie & Son, 1937).

DAWSON, R. B., *Practical Lawncraft* (Crosby Lockwood, 1939).

JOHNS, Rev. C. A., *Flowers of the Field* (Routledge, 1949).

LEWIS, I. G., *Turf* (Faber & Faber, 1948).

LONG, H. C., *Weeds of Grassland* (H.M. Stationery Office).

PERCIVAL, JOHN, *Agricultural Botany* (Duckworth, 1936).

PIPER & OAKLEY, *Turf for Golf Courses* (Macmillan, New York, 1923).

JOURNALS

Board of Greenkeeping Research Journal, published half-yearly.
British Golf Greenkeeper, published monthly.
Golfdom, published monthly (American).
Park Administration, published monthly.
Parks, Golf Courses & Sports Grounds, published monthly.
National Association of Groundsmen Journal, published monthly.
Royal Horticultural Society Journal, published monthly.

BULLETINS AND LEAFLETS

Ministry of Agriculture bulletins.
Welsh Plant Breeding Station bulletins.

Index

INDEX

210